Nine a day

A. L. Griffiths

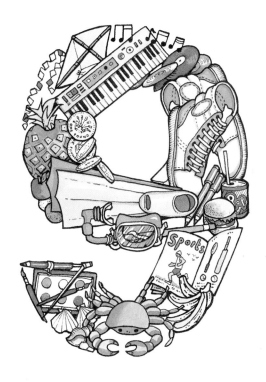

OLIVER & BOYD

Oliver & Boyd
Longman House
Burnt Mill
Harlow
Essex CM20 2JE

An Imprint of Longman Group UK Ltd

ISBN 0 05 003926 1
First published 1987
Fourth impression 1991

Set in 12pt Linotype Melior Roman
Designed and illustrated by Scorpion Pica
Produced by Longman Group (FE) Ltd
Printed in Hong Kong

NUMBER

FRACTIONS

DECIMAL FRACTIONS

MONEY

LENGTH

MASS (WEIGHT)

CAPACITY

TIME

AREA

CHECKING UP

MIXED REVISION

1

A numeral is a name for a number. We use the digits 1, 2, 3, 4, 5, 6, 7, 8 and 9 together with 0 to write numerals. Write a numeral for each of these numbers.

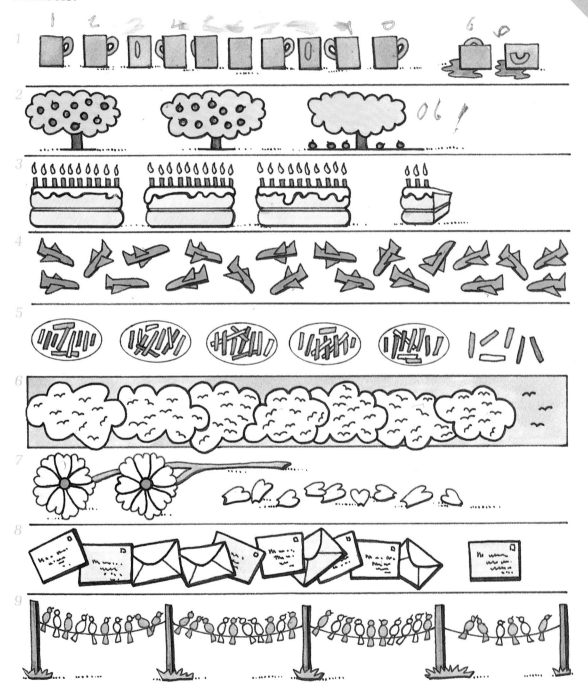

2

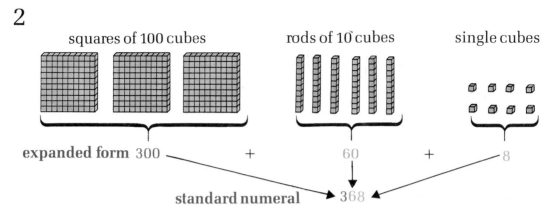

squares of 100 cubes   rods of 10 cubes   single cubes

expanded form 300   +   60   +   8

standard numeral ➤ 368 ◄

Write the standard numeral for each number below.

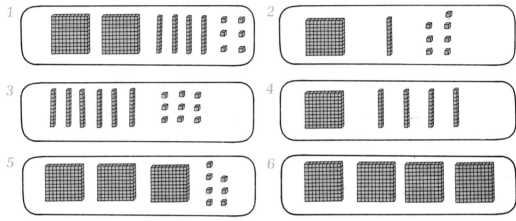

7 Copy and write the missing numerals: 767 = ■ + 60 + ▲.

8 What number is 5 more than 597?

9 What number is 5 less than 403?

3

Write <, > or = in place of each ●.

1 342 ● 243

2 300 + 70 ● 70 + 300

3 909 ● 900 + 90 + 9

4 643 ● 30 + 60 + 400

5 700 + 80 + 6 ● 700 + 60 + 8

6 987 ● 900 + 7 + 80

7 600 + 30 + 7 ● 37 + 600

8 700 + 7 ● 70 + 70

9 50 + 500 + 5 ● 555

4

The numeral for this number is **2314**.

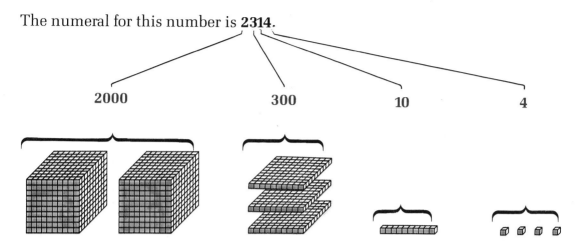

Write the numeral for each of these numbers.

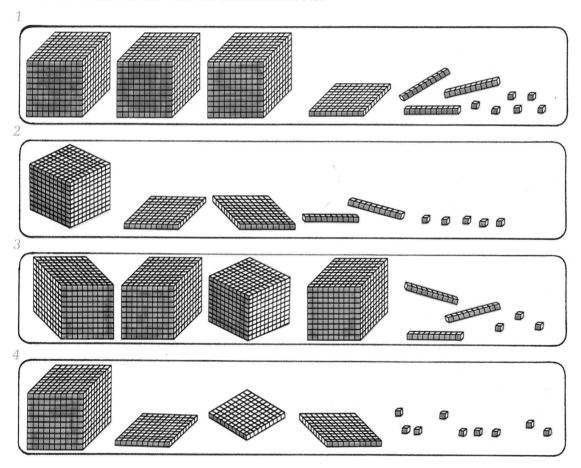

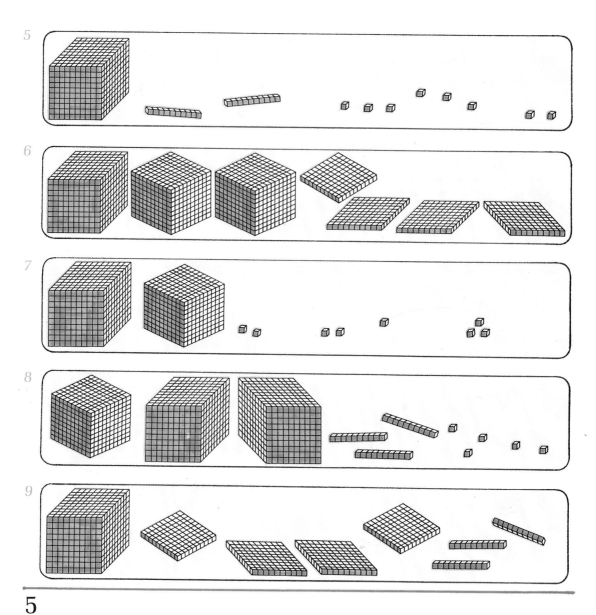

5

We can think of numbers in many different ways.

3725 can be thought of as:

3 thousands and 7 hundreds and 25 units (ones),
372 tens and 5 units,
37 hundreds and 2 tens and 5 units,
37 hundreds and 25 units.

Copy, putting in the missing numerals.

1 $675 = 600 +$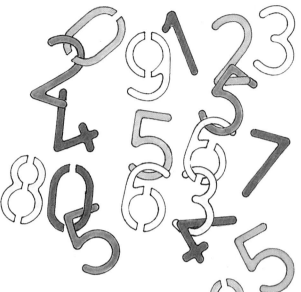
2 $923 = \blacktriangle$ tens $+ 3$
3 $634 = 6$ hundreds $+ \blacktriangle$ tens $+ 4$
4 $5382 = \blacklozenge$ thousands $+ 382$
5 $6495 = \blacktriangledown$ hundreds $+ 95$
6 $4609 = \blacktriangle$ tens $+ 9$
7 $7019 = \blacktriangledown$ hundreds $+ 19$
8 $6351 = \blacklozenge$ thousands $+ 351$
9 $8070 = \blacktriangledown$ hundreds $+ 7$ tens

6

Write the numeral which can be put in place of each ■.

1 $600 + 78 = $ ■
2 $2000 + 49 = $ ■
3 $5000 + 17 = $ ■
4 $7000 + 80 + 4 = $ ■
5 $8000 + 900 + 70 = $ ■
6 $6000 + 500 + 3 = $ ■
7 $500 + (9 \times 10) = $ ■
8 $(26 \times 10) + 16 = $ ■
9 $(37 \times 100) + 28 = $ ■

7

17 hundreds + 2 tens + 7 units = 1727

Write the numeral which can be put in place of each ■.

1 27 hundreds + 3 tens + 4 units = ■
2 6 thousands + 27 units = ■
3 48 hundreds + 3 tens + 7 units = ■
4 426 tens + 8 units = ■
5 4 thousands + 5 tens = ■
6 5 thousands + 25 units = ■
7 38 hundreds + 4 tens + 6 units = ■
8 23 hundreds + 4 units = ■
9 3 thousands + 3 units = ■

8

The numeral for this abacus
number is 40 000

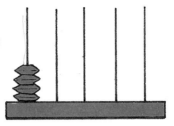

Write a numeral for each of these abacus numbers.

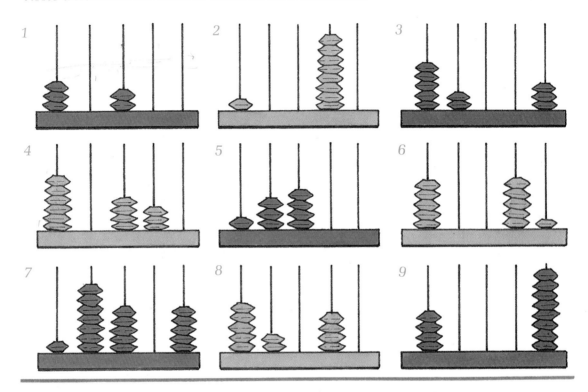

9

Write in digits:

1 sixty thousand, four hundred.
2 nineteen thousand and nineteen.
3 twenty-four thousand, eight hundred and eight.
4 fifty thousand, five hundred.
5 sixty-seven thousand, one hundred and twenty.
6 eighty thousand and eight.
7 twenty thousand, two hundred and two.
8 ninety thousand.
9 sixty thousand and sixty-six.

10

Write the standard numeral for each of these.

1 20 000 + 7000 + 300 + 20 + 6
2 forty thousand + 404
3 58 thousand + 800
4 fifteen thousand + 515
5 66 thousand + 66
6 80 000 + 5000 + 4 hundreds
7 20 000 + 1000 + 90 + 5
8 70 000 + 400 + 30 + 2
9 10 000 + 2000 + 6

11

The number shown on this calculator
is **five hundred and eleven thousand**

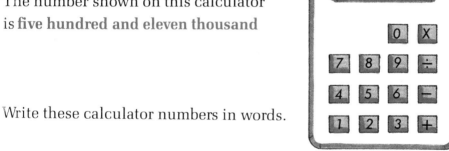

Write these calculator numbers in words.

1

2

3

4

5

6

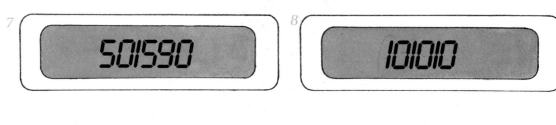

12

Write the missing numerals.

1 400 000 + 60 000 + 7000 + 300 + ? + 8 = 467 358
2 300 000 + 2000 + 300 + 60 + 7 = ?
3 800 000 + ? + 800 + 80 + 8 = 880 888
4 200 000 + 10 000 + 90 + 5 = ?
5 500 000 + ? + 100 + 10 = 501 110
6 900 000 + ? + 70 = 970 070
7 700 000 + 7000 + ? + 7 = 707 077
8 ? + 40 000 + 6000 + 500 + 70 = 646 570
9 200 + 200 000 + 20 + ? = 220 220

13

Write each of these numerals using only digits.

1 304 thousand
2 68 thousand
3 200 thousand
4 one hundred and one thousand
5 eighty thousand
6 seven hundred and eighty thousand
7 four hundred and twenty thousand + 307
8 six hundred and twenty-eight thousand + 91
9 two hundred thousand and twenty

14

Here is the panel of an electric calculator. You can see that it is similar to an abacus, but the calculator uses lights instead of beads to show numbers.

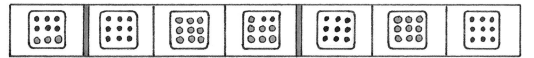

The number shown on the calculator above is:

three million, ninety-seven thousand and ninety

Write the numbers below in words.

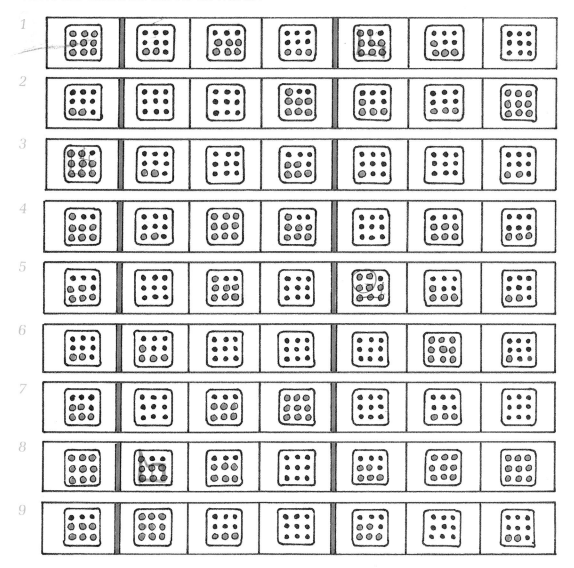

15

1 $1\,000\,000 + 70\,000 + 600 + 23 =$ [   ]

2 Write a numeral for 1000 hundreds.

3 Write this numeral in expanded form.
   [1 020 603]

4 Write >, < or = in place of ◯.

   A thousand thousands ◯ 1 000 000.

5 What is the number shown on this meter?
   Write the number in words.

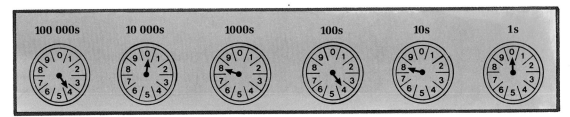

6 Take two hundred and two thousand from 222 222.

7 Take one hundred and one thousand from 1 111 111.

8 Solve this equation: $1\,000\,000 - n = 990\,000$.

9 What is the missing numeral?
   $25 \times ? \times 20 = 500$

16

1 What is the greatest number you can name using each of
   the digits 1, 2, 3, 4, and 5 once only?

2 What is the greatest 5-digit number?

3 What is the least number that can be named using each of the digits
   4, 3, 8 and 6 once only?

4 What is the greatest 4-digit even number?

5 What is the least 3-digit even number that can be named with the
   digits 4, 6, and 3?

6 What is the greatest odd number that can be named using each of the digits
   3, 4, 5, 6, and 7 once only?

7 What number is 1 more than 909 999?

8 What number is 1 less than 999 000?

9 Write in digits the number which is 10 000 more than a million.

17

This test car has completed 1000 laps of this 1000 metre circuit. It has travelled
a **million metres (1 000 000 metres)**

Write in digits:

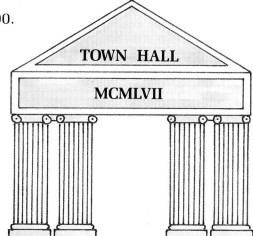

1 twenty million.
2 one million, one hundred thousand.
3 six million, sixty thousand.
4 ninety million.
5 two million, five hundred and twenty-three thousand.
6 seven million, two hundred thousand and fifteen.
7 five million and fifty thousand.
8 four million, one hundred and ten thousand.
9 one million, four hundred and thirty-six thousand, two hundred
   and twenty-five.

18

Give the number that is:

1 a thousand more than 4 623 400.
2 a hundred thousand more than 7 673 000.
3 ten thousand more than 2 438 000.
4 one million more than 637 000.
5 fifty thousand less than 5 550 000.
6 two thousand less than 2 222 000.
7 a million less than 5 407 000.
8 six hundred thousand less than 6 687 000.
9 a thousand less than 1 000 000.

19

To find the value of the number
we must add the value
of the numerals, like this:

M (1000) + **CM** (900) + **L** (50) + **VII** (7)
MCMLVII = 1957

TOWN HALL

MCMLVII

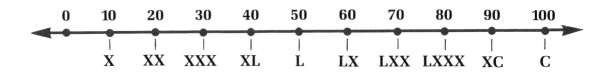

Write these in Roman numerals.

1	47	2	64	3	ninety-nine
4	85	5	33	6	seventy-six

Write these in our numerals.

7	LXXIV	8	XLIX	9	XXIX

20

Look at the number line below.

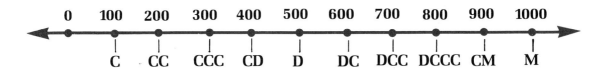

Write these in Roman numerals.

1 268　2 1340　3 five hundred and seventy

4 1900　5 409　6 three hundred and forty-four

Write the dates of the buildings in our numerals.

MDCCCXLI

MDCCX

MDCCCLVII

21

We have already learned that the order in which we add numbers does not affect the sum.

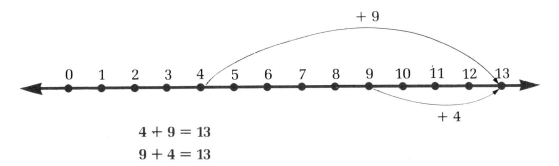

$$4 + 9 = 13$$
$$9 + 4 = 13$$

What does each letter stand for?

1   $9 + 8 = 8 + a$
2   $b + 76 = 76 + 29$
3   $19 + 0 = 0 + c$
4   $609 + n = 608 + 609$

We have also learned that the way the numbers are grouped does not affect the sum.

$$(7 + 6) + 4 \quad \text{or} \quad 7 + (6 + 4)$$
$$13 \quad + 4 \quad \text{or} \quad 7 + \quad 10 = 17$$

Add these.

5   $14 + 15 + 5$
6   $23 + 7 + 9$
7   $9 + 11 + 13 + 7$
8   $42 + 6 + 8$
9   $354 + 70 + 30$

22

Find the sum of:

1   $30 + 40 + 60$
2   $20 + 80 + 90$
3   $230 + 40 + 160$
4   $20 + 80 + 30 + 70$
5   $70 + 80 + 40$
6   $70 + 60 + 90 + 30$
7   $400 + 700 + 300$
8   $800 + 6000 + 4000$
9   $1500 + 900 + 500$

23

Find the sum of:

1 43 and 26

2 42 and 38

3 60 and 81

4 714 and 60

5 90 and 90

6 80 and 520

7 350 and 90

8 130 and 570

9 790 and 120

24

For every addition equation we can think of a subtraction equation.

$4 + 7 = 11$

$11 - 7 = 4$

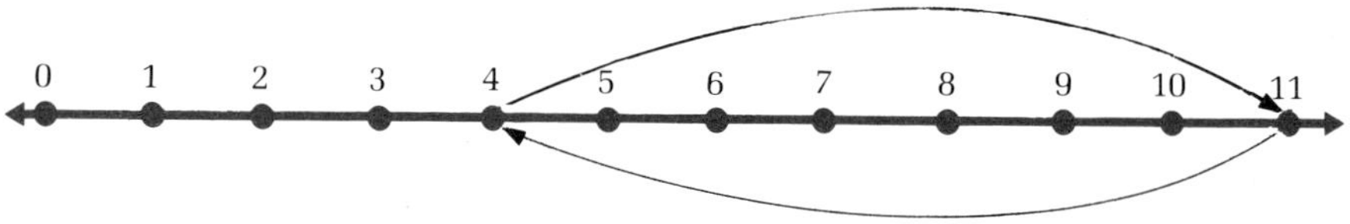

Write a subtraction equation that goes with:

1 $47 + 16 = 63$

2 $38 + 13 = 51$

3 $14 + 18 = 32$

4 $28 + 26 = 54$

5 $78 + 28 = 106$

Write an addition equation that goes with:

6 $73 - 56 = 17$

7 $91 - 24 = 67$

8 $80 - 19 = 61$

9 $72 - 45 = 27$

25

We can check subtraction by addition.

$$\begin{array}{r} 30 \\ -17 \\ \hline 13 \end{array}$$

To check this answer, we find the sum of 13 and 17. If the sum is 30, we know the answer is correct.

$$\begin{array}{r} 17 \\ +13 \\ \hline 30 \end{array}$$

Find the differences between the numbers below and check
the answers by addition.

1 83 and 7
2 110 and 60
3 86 and 41
4 70 and 15
5 43 and 14
6 50 and 27
7 86 and 38
8 800 and 450
9 1000 and 350

26

Write the correct sign ($>$, $<$ or $=$) in place of each ⬤.

1 $710 - 200$ ⬤ $900 - 190$
2 $63 - 18$ ⬤ $73 - 28$
3 $85 - 17$ ⬤ $96 - 24$
4 $60 - 15$ ⬤ $70 - 5$
5 $110 - 30$ ⬤ $140 - 110$
6 $98 + 67$ ⬤ $88 + 97$
7 $450 + 240$ ⬤ $343 + 358$
8 $769 + 176$ ⬤ $679 + 186$
9 $843 + 549$ ⬤ $643 + 579$

27

$$2500 - \boxed{n} = 1200$$

Solve these equations.

1 $2500 - n = 1200$
2 $a + 900 = 3600$
3 $3500 - b = 1700$
4 $1200 + n = 3000$
5 $7040 + 2060 = d$
6 $k - 29 = 86$
7 $m - 40 = 960$
8 $n - 10 = 1090$
9 $p - 90 = 901$

CHECK IT!

28

The map shows the route from Martin's house to the secret headquarters (HQ) with the distances marked in paces.

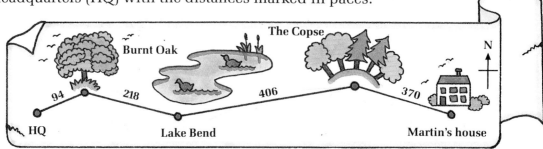

1 What is the distance in paces from HQ to Lake Bend?

2 What is the distance from Burnt Oak to The Copse?

3 What is the distance from Lake Bend to Martin's house?

4 What is the distance from HQ to The Copse?

5 How much farther is it from Lake Bend to The Copse than from Burnt Oak to Lake Bend?

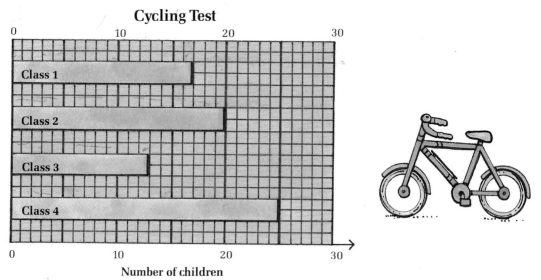

6 How many children altogether in Class 1, 2 and 3 have passed the test?

7 How many more children have passed in Class 4 than Class 3?

8 Seventeen girls have passed the test in Class 4. How many boys in that class have passed?

9 There are 31 children in Class 1. How many have not passed the test?

29

1 Add the difference between 19 and 11 to the sum of 19 and 11.

2 How many more than 60 is the total of 28,7 and 32?

3 The sum of two numbers is a thousand and their difference is a hundred. What are the two numbers?

4 Find the difference between the least and the greatest of these numbers.

| 4044 | 4400 | 4004 | 4404 |

5 From the total of 220, 202 and 222 subtract the difference between the greatest and least of the three numbers.

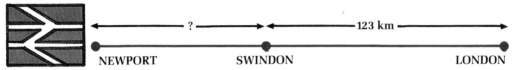

6 The distance from London to Newport by rail is 212 kilometres. What is the distance from Swindon to Newport?

7 By how many is 107 − 37 greater than 43 + 17?

8 The sum of two numbers is 7 less than 100. One number is 48. What is the other number?

9 Write the number which can be put in place of ■ ■ in this addition.

```
    4 0
  ■ ■
+ 8 0
-----
  2 1 0
```

30

1 What is the greatest number you can name, using each of these 7 digits once only?

2 Write in digits the number five hundred and twenty-four thousand, two hundred and forty-seven.

3 Write this date in our numerals.

MCMXXIV

4 Write a numeral for the number that is 100 thousand more than a million.

5 Write + or − in place of each ●.

47 ● 74 = 170 ● 49

6 What is the missing number in this subtraction?

$$\begin{array}{r} \rule{2em}{0.8em} \\ -\ 4\ 9\ 5 \\ \hline 1\ 0\ 5 \end{array}$$

7 Find the sum.

       4 356 704 + 997 + 3

8 Write the missing digit for each ■.

$$\begin{array}{r} 6\ 3\ 4 \\ +\ \blacksquare\ \blacksquare\ \blacksquare \\ \hline 9\ 0\ 0 \end{array}$$

9 Write in digits the sum of eight hundred and eighty and eight thousand and eight.

31

Look at this example:

3 + 3 + 3 = 9
3 times 3 = 9
3 × 3 = 9

  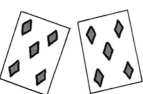

5 + 5 + 5 + 5 = 20
4 × 5 = 20

Write an addition equation and a multiplication equation like the ones shown above for each of these.

1 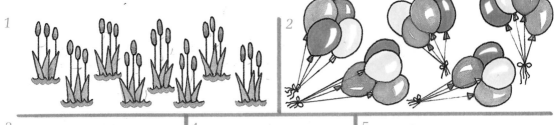

2

3 

4 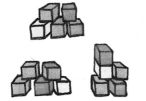

5 

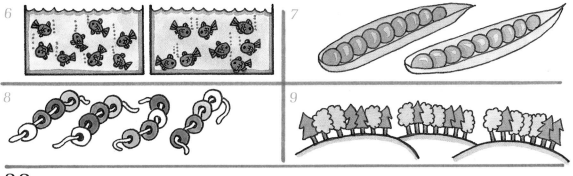

32

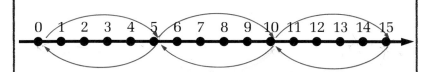

We can see from the number line that

$$5 + 5 + 5 = 15, \quad 3 \times 5 = 15.$$

We can also see from the number line that

$$15 - 5 - 5 - 5 = 0, \quad 15 \div 5 = 3.$$

Write a multiplication equation and a division equation
for each of these number lines.

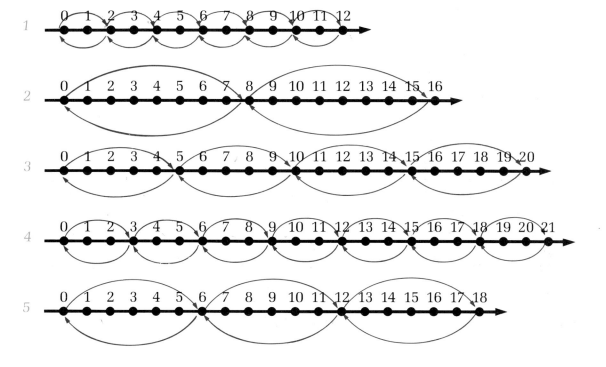

6 Write a multiplication equation for
9 + 9 + 9 + 9.

7 Write a multiplication equation for
8 + 8 + 8 + 8 + 8 + 8 + 8.

8 Write a multiplication equation for
7 + 7 + 7 + 7 + 7 + 7.

9 Write a multiplication equation for
6 + 6 + 6 + 6 + 6 + 6 + 6 + 6 + 6.

33

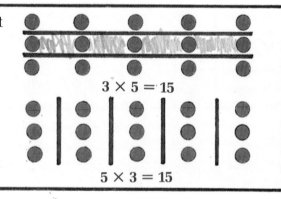

We can see from this arrangement
of dots that there are
3 rows of 5.

$3 \times 5 = 15$

We can also see that there are
5 columns of 3.

$5 \times 3 = 15$

Write two multiplication equations for each of the pictures below.

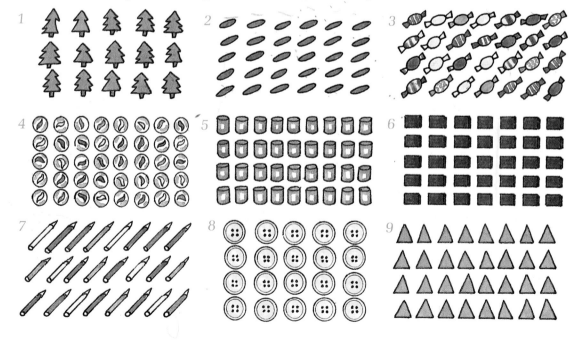

34

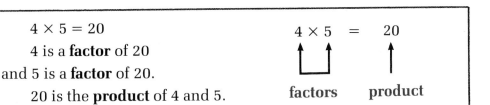

$4 \times 5 = 20$

4 is a **factor** of 20

and 5 is a **factor** of 20.

20 is the **product** of 4 and 5.

$4 \times 5 = 20$

factors   product

Solve each of these equations by finding the missing factor.

1 $n \times 9 = 72$

2 $4 \times n = 36$

3 $n \times 11 = 77$

4 $\blacksquare \times 10 = 10$

5 $6 \times \blacksquare = 54$

6 $8 \times \blacksquare = 40$

Solve each of these equations by finding the product.

7 $7 \times 7 = \blacksquare$

8 $9 \times 9 = x$

9 $8 \times 9 = a$

35

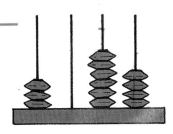

1 Add 36 to this abacus number and write the answer in words.

2 What is the greatest 4-digit number you can write without using any digit more than once?

3 Find the missing factor in this equation.

$$170 = 17 \times 2 \times n$$

4 The difference between two numbers is 30 and their sum is 110. What are the numbers?

5 From the product of 6 and 7 subtract their sum.

6 Write the correct sign ($<$, $>$ or $=$) for .

$$350 + 450 \;\bullet\; 1000 - 250$$

7 Write out this subtraction in full.

$$\begin{array}{r} \blacksquare\,7 \\ -\ 4\ 8 \\ \hline 2\ \blacksquare \end{array}$$

8 $869 + 98 = \blacksquare$

9 Write a multiplication equation for this addition.

$$7 + 7 + 7 + 7 + 7 + 7 + 7 + 7 + 7$$

36

We have already learned that the order in which we add numbers does not affect the sum. Does the order in which we multiply factors affect the product?

Solve these equations.

1 $9 \times 6 = n \times 9$

2 $n \times 4 = 4 \times 7$

3 $8 \times 9 = 9 \times n$

4 $63 \times 48 = n \times 63$

When we multiply we can 'split' a factor like this:

$$7 \times 8 = (2 \times 8) + (5 \times 8).$$

Solve these equations.

5 $9 \times 7 = (6 \times 7) + (n \times 7)$

6 $8 \times 9 = (5 \times 9) + (n \times 9)$

7 $n \times 6 = (5 \times 6) + (4 \times 6)$

8 $67 \times 16 = (67 \times 12) + (67 \times n)$

9 $n \times 39 = (9 \times 39) + (11 \times 39)$

37

1 How many boxes like this would you need for 36 paper cups?

2 How many boxes like this would you need for 42 cans of juice?

Joyful Juice

3 There are 48 choc ices altogether in these boxes. How many ices are there in each box?

Choc Ices Choc Ices Choc Ices Choc Ices Choc Ices Choc Ices

4 There are 8 cubes in each box. How many cubes are there altogether in these boxes?

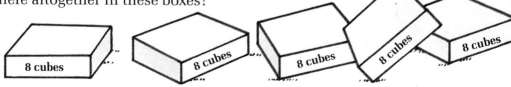

8 cubes 8 cubes 8 cubes 8 cubes 8 cubes

5 There are the same number in each bag and there are 72 marbles altogether.
How many are in a bag?

6 There are 160 pencils altogether and there are the same number in each box.
How many are in a box?

72 marbles are placed in 8 bags with the same number in each.
How many marbles were put in each?

$$72 \div 8 = 9$$

Write a multiplication or division equation like the one above for
each of these problems.

7 Salim has 56 stamps in his album. If he has 7 full pages, how many
stamps are on each page?

8 Paul has 7 sets of cards. There are 9 in each set. How many cards
does he have?

9 Claire has 55p. How many coloured pencils costing 11p each can she buy?

38

> 7 × 10 means 7 tens   7 × 100 means 7 hundreds
> = 70   = 700
> 7 × 1000 means 7 thousands
> = 7000

Find the products.

1 6×100

2 9×100

3 23×10

4 48×10

5 32×1000

Find the other factor.

6 $130 = n \times 10$

7 $3600 = a \times 100$

8 $900 = x \times 100$

9 $1500 = 100 \times n$

39

> 6 × 80 or 80 × 6 means 48 tens = 480
>
> 3 × 900 or 900 × 3 means 27 hundreds = 2700

1   7 × 60   = ■

2   8 × 90   = ■

3   800 × 2   = ■

4   6 × 400   = ■

5   ■ × 700 = 3500

6   4000 × ■ = 20 000

7   5600 ÷ 7 = ■

8   6300 ÷ 9 = ■

9   640 ÷ 80 = ■

40

1 Find the sum of 2 million + 34 thousand + 17 and write the answer in digits.

2 Write out this subtraction in full.

$$\begin{array}{r} 3\ \ 2\ \ 5 \\ -\ ■\ ■\ 7 \\ \hline 1\ \ 5\ \ 8 \end{array}$$

3 Write <, > or = in place of ●.

     3 × 1000 × 100 ● 3 × 1 000 000

4 Solve this equation: 28 + 28 = 7 × (5 + **n**).

5 What is the sum of (18 × 5) and (2 × 5)?

6 How many pieces of gingerbread are there in six trays?

7 How much more would I pay for 9 pencils at 10p each than 7 pencils at 7p each?

8 I am thinking of a certain number. Twice the number is equal to three times six. What is the number?

9 10 000 ÷ 100 = ■

41

When we use letters in place of numbers, we can show multiplication without using the multiplication sign ($\times$).

$4n$ means $4 \times n$

1 If $c = 7$, what is $4c + 2$?
2 If $n = 9$, what is $40 - 2n$?
3 If $a = 15$, what is $2a + 7$?
4 What is $90 \div 2c$, when $c = 15$?
5 What is $3x - 3$, when $x = 12$?
6 What is $\frac{d}{7} + 3$, when $d = 56$?
7 If $y = 13$, what is $3y - 9$?
8 If $x = 9$, what is $11x + 9x$?
9 If $m = 7$, what is $2m + 7m - 10$?

42

Write the number sentence that will help you to solve the problem,

like this: ten divided by a certain number equals five.

$$\frac{10}{x} = 5 \text{ or } 10 \div x = 5$$

Then solve the equation $\rightarrow x = 2$

Call the unknown number x.
1 Twelve added to a certain number equals twenty.
2 Four multiplied by some number equals twenty-four.
3 Some number divided by seven equals five.
4 A certain number subtracted from fifty equals thirty.
5 Fourteen subtracted from some number is sixteen.
6 A certain number is equal to seven multiplied by eight.
7 Some number divided by nine equals nine.
8 Three times a certain number plus six equals eighteen.
9 Twice a certain number divided by three is six.

43

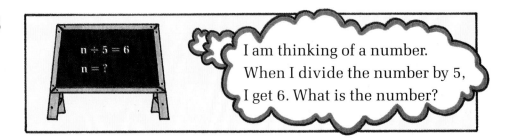

Write an equation for each of these puzzles, then find the solution.
Call the unknown number **n**.

1 I am thinking of a number. When I add 16 to it, I get 30. What is the number?

2 I am thinking of a number. When I subtract 23 from it, I get 37.
  What is the number?

3 I am thinking of a number. When I multiply it by 6, I get 240.
  What is the number?

4 I am thinking of a number. When I divide it by 6, I get 50. What is the number?

5 In thirteen years time Karen will be 22. How old is she now?

6 Raj is 23 cm taller than Ann who is 129 cm tall. How tall is Raj?

7 When I add a number to itself then add 10, I get 36.
  What is my number?

8 After losing 17 marbles, John found he had 17 left.
  How many did he have at first?

9 Five times a number plus 6 is equal to 51. What is the number?

44

Solve these equations.

1 $n + 43 = 80$ 2 $5x = 465$

3 $(4 \times n) + 8 = 56$ 4 $2x + 1 = 19$

5 $2x - 3 = 15$ 6 $(x \div 4) + 5 = 12$

7 $17 = y - 13$ 8 $\frac{y}{4} = 12 - 7$

9 $2n = 18 - 4$

You must
CHECK
each solution.

45

1 Write in digits the number which is half a million more than 555 555.

2 What is the quotient when 300 is divided by 20?

3 $77 - 7 - 7 - 7 - 7 - 7 - 7 - 7 - 7 - 7 - 7 = $ ■

4 Find the sum of (18 × 7) and (7 × 2).

5 Write the correct sign (>, < or =) in place of ●.

  954 ● (9 × 100) + (6 × 10) + 4

6 13 + 11 + 19 + 17 + 18 = ■

7 The sum of four numbers is 100. Three of the numbers are 35, 15 and 25. What is the other number?

8 What is the product of 50 and 200?

9 There are 7 boys left after picking 3 rugby teams (15 players in a rugby team). How many boys are there altogether?

46

> We already learned that when we multiply we can 'split' factors. We also know that we can multiply factors in any order and get the same product.
>
> 50 × 30 = 5 × 10 × 3 × 10 = 15 × 100 = 1500

Find these products or factors.

Use your calculator to check the answers.

1 90 × 20 = 9 × 10 × 2 × 10 = ■ 2 70 × 30 = 7 × 10 × 3 × 10 = ■

3 40 × 70 = ■ 4 300 × 40 = ■

5 50 × ■ = 1500 6 40 × 20 = 800

7 4200 ÷ 70 = ■   800 ÷ 40 = ■

8 $\frac{1600}{20}$ = ■ 9 ■ × 90 = 8100

47

> 24 × 3 = (**20** × 3) + (**4** × 3) = 72

Find these products.

1 26 × 6 = ■ 2 63 × 5 = ■ 3 90 × 17 = ■

4 37 × 3 = ■ 5 14 × 20 = ■ 6 16 × 30 = ■

7 52 × 4 = ■ 8 40 × 23 = ■ 9 100 × 87 = ■

48

7, 9, 11, 13, 15, 17, 19 , 21 , 23 , 25

Look at the row of numbers above. The numbers follow a pattern. When the pattern is discovered, it is easy to continue the numbers.

Here is another row of numbers which follows a different pattern.

4, 8, 9, 18, 19, 38 , 39 , 78 , 79

Number patterns like these are called **sequences**.

Give the next four numbers in each sequence.

1 4, 8, 12, 16, 20, ■, ■, ■, ■

2 3, 0, 6, 0, 9, ■, ■, ■, ■

3 7, 18, 29, 40, 51, ■, ■, ■, ■

4 11, 24, 37, 50, 63, ■, ■, ■, ■

5 1, 22, 43, 64, 85, ■, ■, ■, ■

6 1, 1, 2, 3, 5, ■, ■, ■, ■

7 1, 2, 4, 8, 16, ■, ■, ■, ■

8 2, 3, 2, 6, 2, 9, 2, ■, ■, ■, ■

9 1, 7, 1, 14, 1, 21, ■, ■, ■, ■

49

Robin has 6 picture stickers,
John has 1 and David 5.
If they put their stickers
together, then shared them
equally, they would each have 4.

$(6 + 1 + 5) \div 3 = 4$

The **average** of 6, 1 and 5 is **4**.

Robin	🔍 🔪 🪐 🚶 🚀 🏑
John	🔺
David	💫 🚀 ✈ 🔵 🎈
Robin	🔵 🔍 🏑 🔪
John	✈ 🚶 🎈 🔺
David	🪐 💫 🚀 🚀

1 This bar chart shows the number of library books read by some girls. What is the average number of books read by a girl?

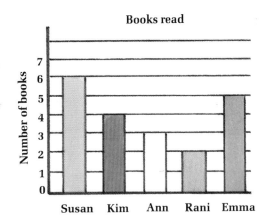

Books read

Here are the marks gained by Sam and Sue during a swimming test.

	Sam	Sue
Diving test	4	5
Life saving	10	5
Swimming test	7	8

2 What is Sam's average score?
3 What is Sue's average score?

4 What is the average weight of Jane, Ann, Alan and Peter?
5 What is the average height of Jane, Ann, Alan and Peter?

	Height in centimetres	Weight in kilograms
Jane	140	40
Ann	130	38
Alan	160	50
Peter	170	52

6 Find the average of these numbers.

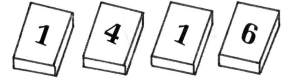

7 During a fortnight's holiday I walked an average of eight kilometres a day. How many kilometres was this altogether?
8 What is the average age of the children in this family? Kevin is 7 years, Sarah is 12 years, Mark is 14 years and Karen 3 years.
9 Seven children collected an average of seventeen conkers. How many conkers did they collect altogether?

1 Write in words 4 004 040.

2 The sum of two numbers is a thousand.
One of the numbers is 350.
What is the difference between the two numbers?

3 Ali has 21 marbles, David 12 and Mohammed 27.
They each gave a third of their marbles to Raj.
How many marbles did Raj get?

4 What number is covered in the multiplication on
the blackboard?

5 Write the correct sign (>, < or =) in place of ●.
(100 − 5) × 3 ● 3 × 95

6 Write the next two numbers in this sequence.
390, 371, 352, 333, ■, ■, . . .

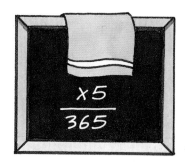

7 Divide the product of 9 and 36 by 4.

8 In a school dining room three hundred
children sat six to a table.
How many full tables were there?

9 Write in Roman numerals the average of these numbers.

| C | V | V | L |

51

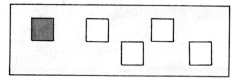 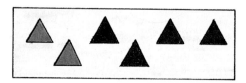

1 of the **5** squares $\frac{1}{5}$ is
coloured.
One-fifth of the squares
is coloured.

2 of the **6** triangles $\frac{2}{6}$ are
coloured.
Two-sixths of the
triangles are coloured.

Look at these pictures and then write a fraction for the part that is orange.

Write each fraction in digits, then in words like this:
$\frac{1}{5}$, one-fifth

1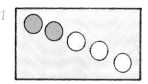

2

3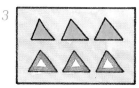

4

5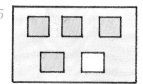

6

7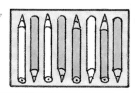

8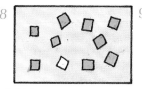

9

52

Each piece is $\frac{1}{4}$, **one-quarter**, of the pie.

Three pieces are $\frac{3}{4}$, **three-quarters** of the pie.

Write a fraction to show:

    a the part of the whole which is orange,

    b the part of the whole which is blue.

1

2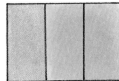

3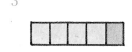

4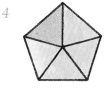

5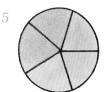

6

7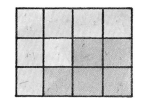

8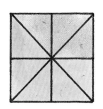

9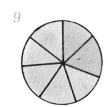

53

We can see that **3** of the **6** fruits, that is $\frac{3}{6}$, are bananas. We can also see that **1** of the **2** sets of fruit, that is $\frac{1}{2}$, are bananas.

$\frac{3}{6}$ **is equivalent to** $\frac{1}{2}$

$$\frac{3}{6} = \frac{1}{2}$$

Can you think of two equivalent fractions to match each of these pictures?

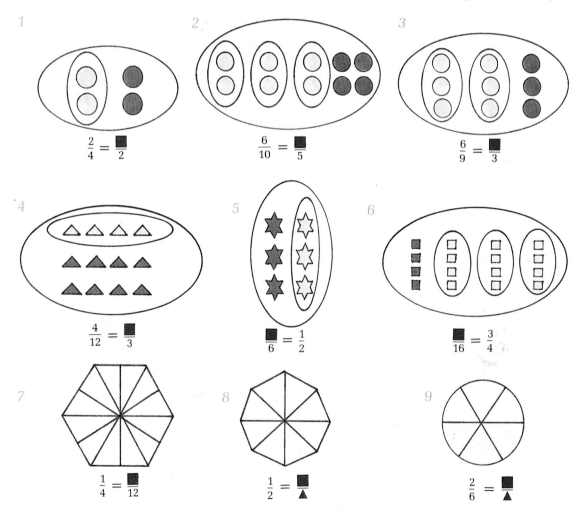

1    $\frac{2}{4} = \frac{\blacksquare}{2}$

2    $\frac{6}{10} = \frac{\blacksquare}{5}$

3    $\frac{6}{9} = \frac{\blacksquare}{3}$

4    $\frac{4}{12} = \frac{\blacksquare}{3}$

5    $\frac{\blacksquare}{6} = \frac{1}{2}$

6    $\frac{\blacksquare}{16} = \frac{3}{4}$

7    $\frac{1}{4} = \frac{\blacksquare}{12}$

8    $\frac{1}{2} = \frac{\blacksquare}{\blacktriangle}$

9    $\frac{2}{6} = \frac{\blacksquare}{\blacktriangle}$

54

Write out each of these
in full like this:

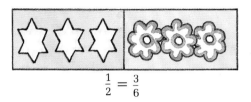

$\frac{1}{2} = \frac{3}{6}$

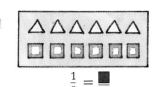

1

$\frac{1}{2} = \frac{\blacksquare}{12}$

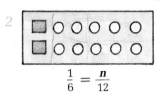

2

$\frac{1}{6} = \frac{n}{12}$

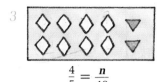

3

$\frac{4}{5} = \frac{n}{10}$

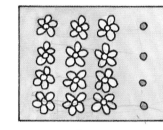

4

$\frac{3}{4} = \frac{n}{16}$

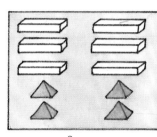

5

$\frac{3}{5} = \frac{n}{10}$

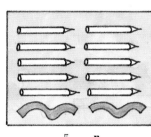

6

$\frac{5}{6} = \frac{n}{12}$

7

$\frac{2}{3} = \frac{n}{18}$

8

$\frac{2}{3} = \frac{n}{15}$

9

$\frac{2}{3} = \frac{n}{9}$

55

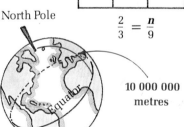

North Pole

10 000 000
metres

1 Write in words the distance marked on the globe.

2 Write =, > or < in place of ●.

$541 + 896 \; ● \; 696 + 741$

3 If the product is 360 and one factor is 20, what is the other factor?

4 Solve this equation: $(3 \times 9) + (n \times 9) = 63$.

5 Which of these is true?

   a $\frac{450}{15} > \frac{600}{20}$

   b $450 \div 15 < 600 \div 20$

   c $450 \div 15 = 600 \div 20$

6 Write out this multiplication
   in full.

$$\begin{array}{r} 9\,\blacksquare \\ \times\ 7 \\ \hline \blacksquare\,\blacksquare\,3 \end{array}$$

7 $67 \times 9 = 603$, so $670 \times 90 = \blacksquare$

8 What is the average height?

	Height (cm)
Usha	120
Ravi	170
Jenny	160

9 $4 \times 37 \times 25 = \blacksquare$

56

What fraction is:

1 1 day of a week?
2 3 days of a week?
3 1 hour of a day?
4 5 hours of a day?
5 1 minute of an hour?
6 9 of 20?

7 In a class of 28 pupils, 13 are girls. What fraction of the pupils are boys?

8 Rani has spent 13p out of 20p. What fraction of her money does she have left?

9 A boy bought a packet of 12 toffee chews. He ate 7 chews. What fraction does he have left?

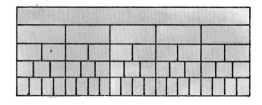

57

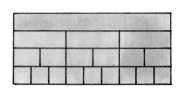

Use the drawings to help you to write the equations in full.

1 $\dfrac{3}{4} = \dfrac{\blacksquare}{8} = \dfrac{\blacktriangle}{16}$

2 $\dfrac{2}{3} = \dfrac{\blacksquare}{6} = \dfrac{\blacktriangle}{9}$

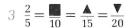

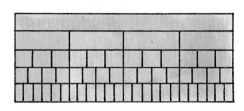

3 $\dfrac{2}{5} = \dfrac{\blacksquare}{10} = \dfrac{\blacktriangle}{15} = \dfrac{\blacktriangledown}{20}$

4 $\dfrac{1}{4} = \dfrac{\blacksquare}{12} = \dfrac{\blacktriangle}{16} = \dfrac{\blacktriangledown}{24}$

5 $\dfrac{1}{3} = \dfrac{\blacksquare}{9}$

6 $\dfrac{3}{5} = \dfrac{\blacksquare}{20}$

7 $\dfrac{4}{5} = \dfrac{\blacksquare}{15}$

8 $\dfrac{3}{4} = \dfrac{\blacksquare}{24}$

9 $\dfrac{1}{2} = \dfrac{\blacksquare}{16}$

58

Write these equations in full.

1 $\frac{3}{5} = \frac{\blacksquare}{10}$

2 $\frac{1}{8} = \frac{\blacksquare}{24}$

3 $\frac{2}{3} = \frac{\blacksquare}{15}$

4 $\frac{\blacksquare}{8} = \frac{3}{4}$

5 $\frac{5}{\blacksquare} = \frac{1}{2}$

6 $\frac{5}{6} = \frac{10}{\blacksquare}$

7 $\frac{20}{30} = \frac{2}{\blacksquare}$

8 $\frac{5}{7} = \frac{\blacksquare}{21}$

9 $\frac{\blacksquare}{5} = \frac{12}{15}$

59

$\frac{1}{3}$ of 12 = 4	○ ○ ○ ○ ○ ○ ○ ○ ○ ○ ○ ○	12 ÷ 3 = 4

Write the correct number in place of each ■.

1 One-eighth of 24 = ■

2 One-tenth of 120 = ■

3 $\frac{1}{4}$ of 16 = ■

4 $\frac{1}{7} \times 35$ = ■

5 $\frac{1}{6} \times 54$ = ■

6 $\frac{1}{20} \times 200$ = ■

7 $\frac{1}{9} \times 720$ = ■

8 $\frac{1}{7} \times 560$ = ■

9 $\frac{1}{6} \times 600$ = ■

60

1 Write the score in words.

2 If $n + 501 = 1000$, then $n = $ ■

3 $20\,000 \div 40 = $ ■

4 Write the next two numbers in this sequence.

   38, 57, 76, ■, ■

5 The average of 2, $3\frac{1}{2}$, 3 and $1\frac{1}{2}$ is ■.

6 $100 - 3 - 6 - 7 - 4 - 20 = $ ■

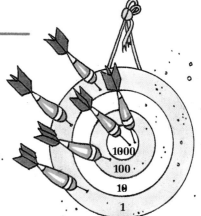

7 $(6 \times 36) + (4 \times 36) =$ ▇

8 $101 \times 30 =$ ▇

9 Here is a page from Donna's coin album. What fraction of the page still has to be filled?

61

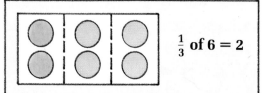

$\frac{1}{3}$ **of 6 = 2**

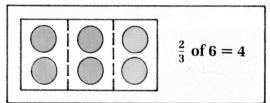

$\frac{2}{3}$ **of 6 = 4**

Now try these.

1 $\frac{2}{5}$ of 10   2 $\frac{5}{7}$ of 14   3 $\frac{3}{5}$ of 20

4 $\frac{3}{4}$ of 28   5 $\frac{2}{3}$ of 15   6 $\frac{5}{6}$ of 18

7 $\frac{3}{8}$ of 16   8 $\frac{7}{8}$ of 24   9 $\frac{2}{9}$ of 27

62

> In the fraction $\frac{3}{4}$ we know that 3 is the **numerator** of the fraction and 4 is the **denominator**. The numerator and denominator are called the **terms** of the fraction.

When both the numerator and the denominator can be divided by a number greater than 1, the fraction is not in its lowest terms. $\frac{15}{20}$ is not its lowest terms, because 5 will divide into 15 and 20.

> $\frac{15}{20}$ in its **lowest terms** is $\frac{3}{4}$

Write these fractions in their lowest terms.

1 $\frac{40}{80}$ 2 $\frac{24}{36}$ 3 $\frac{8}{40}$ 4 $\frac{77}{110}$ 5 $\frac{18}{20}$ 6 $\frac{28}{32}$ 7 $\frac{36}{45}$ 8 $\frac{42}{49}$ 9 $\frac{30}{42}$

63

Write these fractions in their **lowest terms**.

What fraction of:

1   18 is 6?

2   100 is 70?

3   fifty is fifteen?

4   a century is 40 years?

5   an hour is 10 minutes?

6   a day is 4 hours?

7   £1 is 20p?

8   a ten is 6p?

9   a fifty is 25p?

$$\frac{\overset{2}{\cancel{4}}}{\underset{5}{\cancel{10}}} = \frac{2}{5}$$

64

> Numbers like $1\frac{1}{2}$, $2\frac{3}{4}$, $9\frac{1}{5}$ . . . are called **mixed numbers**.

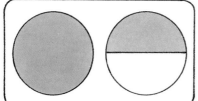 $1\frac{1}{2}$

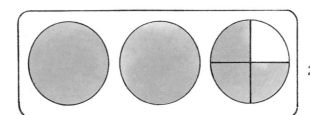 $2\frac{3}{4}$

Write a mixed number for each of these.

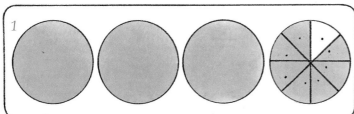

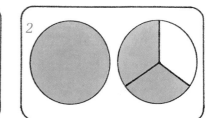

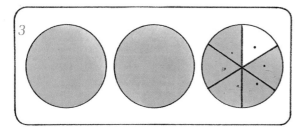

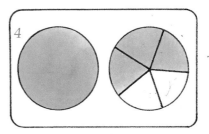

Write out the equations below in full, like this:

$$2\frac{1}{4} = \frac{9}{4}$$

5 $3\frac{2}{3} = \frac{\blacksquare}{3}$

6 $4\frac{7}{8} = \frac{\blacksquare}{8}$

7 $3\frac{9}{10} = \frac{\blacksquare}{10}$

8 $4\frac{1}{6} = \frac{\blacksquare}{6}$

9 $2\frac{2}{7} = \frac{\blacksquare}{7}$

65

1 How many thousands are there in three-quarters of a million?

2 A rocket travelled 143 kilometres in 11 seconds. How many kilometres per second is this?

3 The product of two numbers is 48. The sum of the two numbers is $\frac{1}{3}$ of 48. What are the numbers?

4 The average number of girls in each of the 10 classes of Grove School is 18. The average number of boys in each class is 12. How many pupils are there in the school?

5 Write the correct sign ($>$, $<$ or $=$) in place of each ●.

a $\frac{7}{8}$ ● $\frac{15}{16}$ b $\frac{8}{3}$ ● $2\frac{2}{3}$

6 Twenty-four of the children in an ice-skating club are ten years of age or over. If one-third of the children are under ten years, how many are in the club?

7 Remember that in multiplication we can change the grouping of factors. Write the correct number in place of ■.

$$5 \times 19 \times 2 \times 10 = \blacksquare$$

8 How many model cars do Martin, Peter, Tom and Sam have altogether?

9 What is the average number of cars owned by a boy?

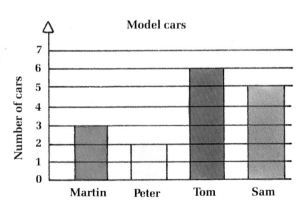

66

On the first abacus the **point** separates the whole numbers from
the fractions.

We can write this abacus number in two ways:

$21\frac{7}{10}$ or 21·7 (we say **twenty-one point seven**).

↑
decimal
point

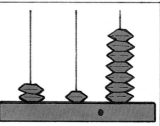

The number on the second abacus is

$42\frac{3}{10}$ or 42·3 (we say **forty-two point three**).

42·3 is called a **decimal fraction** or just
a **decimal**.

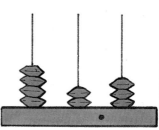

Write these abacus numbers as decimal fractions.

1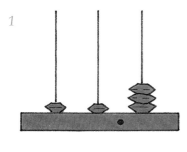
2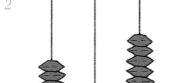
3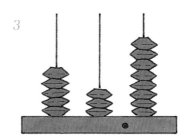

4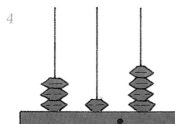
5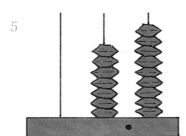
6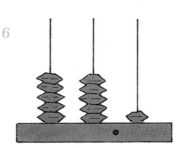

Write these as decimal fractions.

7 forty-eight and seven-tenths

8 $19\frac{1}{10}$ 9 $20\frac{3}{10}$

67

The circle on the right has been divided into ten equal parts.

Each part is one-tenth, $\frac{1}{10}$, of the whole circle.

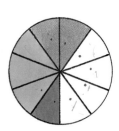

$\frac{1}{10}$ written as a decimal is **0·1**.

$\frac{3}{10}$ or 0·3 of this circle is coloured orange.

1 What decimal fraction of the circle is coloured blue?

2 What decimal fraction of the circle is left blank?

3 What decimal fraction of the circle is red?

What decimal fraction of each of these drawings is orange?

4 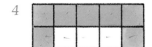   5 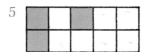   6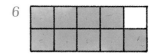

In the picture below we can see there are 3 whole circles and $\frac{4}{10}$ shaded.

This can be written $3\frac{4}{10}$ or in decimal form, 3·4.

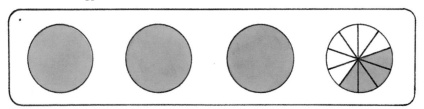

Write in decimal form the whole circles and parts of circles that are orange.

7 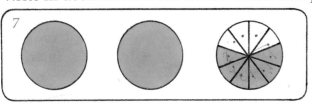   8

9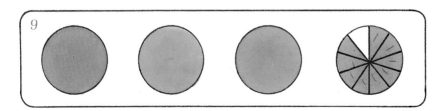

68

The number shown on this abacus is $43\frac{1}{10}$ or $43\frac{10}{100}$.
In decimal form we write $43 \cdot 1$.

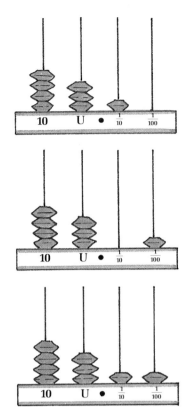

The number shown on this abacus is $43\frac{1}{100}$. In decimal form we write $43 \cdot 01$.

The number shown on this abacus is $43\frac{11}{100}$. In decimal form we write $43 \cdot 11$.

Write these abacus numbers in decimal form.

1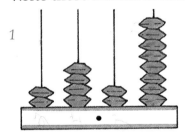

2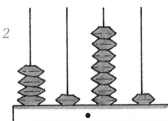

3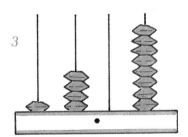

Write out these equations in full.

4 $6 \cdot 34 = 6 + \frac{3}{10} + \frac{\blacksquare}{100} = 6\,\frac{\blacktriangle}{100}$

5 $7 \cdot 14 = 7 + \frac{\blacksquare}{10} + \frac{4}{100} = 7\,\frac{\blacktriangle}{100}$

6 $9 \cdot 68 = 9 + \frac{\blacksquare}{10} + \frac{\blacktriangledown}{100} = 9\,\frac{\blacktriangle}{100}$

7 $4 \cdot 19 = 4 + \frac{1}{\blacksquare} + \frac{9}{\blacktriangledown} = 4\,\frac{\blacktriangle}{\blacktriangledown}$

8 $2 \cdot 03 = 2 + \frac{3}{\blacksquare} = 2\,\frac{\blacktriangle}{\blacksquare}$

9 $3 \cdot 4\ \ = 3 + \frac{\blacktriangledown}{\blacktriangle} = 3\,\frac{\blacktriangledown}{\blacktriangle}$

69

This large square has been divided into a hundred small squares. Each small square is one hundredth ($\frac{1}{100}$) of the large square.

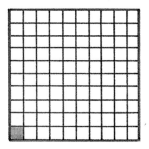

> $\frac{1}{100}$ written as a decimal is **0·01**.

What decimal fraction of each of these large squares is

 a coloured?   b not coloured?

1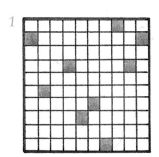

2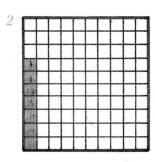

3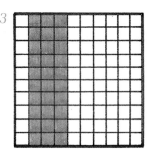

4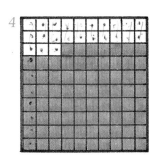

5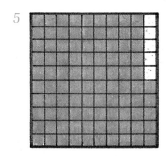

6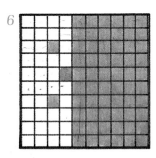

7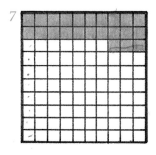

8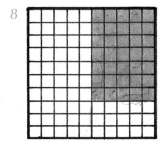

9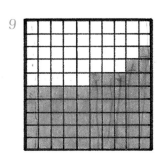

70

1 The distance from the earth to the sun is 150 000 000
   kilometres. Write this number in words.

2 Find one-sixth of one thousand two hundred and write the answer in digits.

3 Write the number which can be written in place of each ■ in this sequence.

   $2\frac{3}{8}, 2\frac{1}{2}, 2\frac{5}{8}, 2\frac{3}{4},$ ■, ■

4 Solve this equation: $72 \div 8 = 8b$.

5 Find the sum of all the factors of 12 (not including 1 and 12).

6 Write $2\frac{7}{100}$ as a decimal fraction.

7 Usha has 30 records. Three-fifths of the records are pop music and the rest
   classical music. How many classical music records does she have?

8 Write this equation in full.

   $5\frac{5}{6} = \frac{■}{6}$

9 What fraction of this circle is orange?
   Write the fraction in its lowest terms.

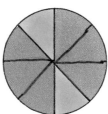

71

We already know that the first place to the right of the decimal point shows the
number of **tenths**

We also know that the second place to the right of the decimal point shows the
number of **hundredths**

The third place to the right of the decimal point shows the number of
thousandths

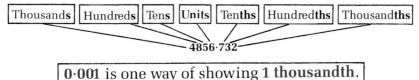

| Thousands | Hundreds | Tens | Units | Tenths | Hundredths | Thousandths |

4856·732

0·001 is one way of showing **1 thousandth**.

Complete the sentences below, like this:

0·58 means 5 tenths and 8 hundredths or 58 hundredths.

1 0·37 means ■ tenths and ▲ hundredths or ◆ hundredths.

2 0·65 means ■ tenths and ▲ hundredths or ◆ hundredths.

3 0·467 means ■ tenths ▲ hundredths and ◆ thousandths or ▼ thousandths.

4 0·963 means ■ tenths or ▲ hundredths and ◆ thousandths or ▼ thousandths.

5 0·603 means ■ tenths and ▲ thousandths or ◆ thousandths.

6 0·037 means ■ hundredths and ▲ thousandths or ◆ thousandths.

7 $0·48 = \dfrac{a}{10} + \dfrac{b}{100} = \dfrac{c}{100}$

8 $0·763 = \dfrac{a}{10} + \dfrac{b}{100} + \dfrac{c}{1000} = \dfrac{d}{1000}$

9 $0·069 = \dfrac{■}{100} + \dfrac{▲}{1000} = \dfrac{◆}{1000}$

72

Write the statements below in full, like this:

$$0·7 = \frac{7}{10} = \frac{70}{100} = \frac{700}{1000}$$

1 $0·3 = \dfrac{■}{10} = \dfrac{▲}{100} = \dfrac{◆}{1000}$

2 $0·19 = \dfrac{■}{10} + \dfrac{▲}{100} = \dfrac{◆}{100} = \dfrac{▼}{1000}$

3 $0·09 = \dfrac{■}{100} = \dfrac{▲}{1000}$

$$0·436 = \frac{4}{10} + \frac{3}{100} + \frac{6}{1000} = \frac{436}{1000}$$

4 $0·786 = \dfrac{■}{1000}$

5 $0·019 = \dfrac{■}{1000}$

6 $0·506 = \dfrac{■}{1000}$

7 $0·78 = \dfrac{■}{1000}$

8 $0·007 = \dfrac{■}{1000}$

9 $0·09 = \dfrac{■}{1000}$

73

We can see there are 2 large squares and $\frac{23}{100}$ shaded. This can be written $2\frac{23}{100}$ or in decimal form, $2\cdot23$.

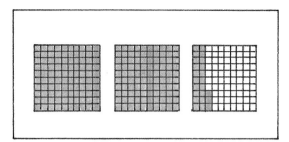

Write these in decimal form.

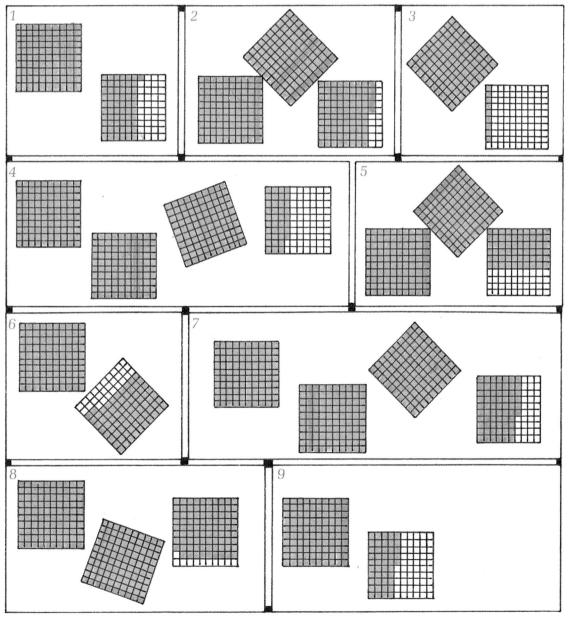

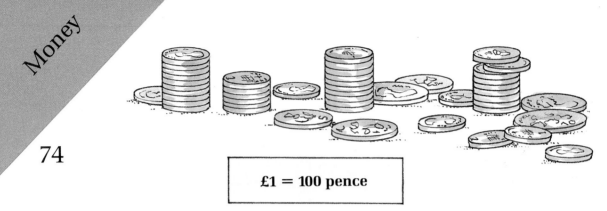

$$\boxed{£1 = 100 \text{ pence}}$$

£3·29 (£3 $\frac{29}{100}$) means **3 pounds and 29 pence**. We say **three pounds twenty-nine**

Write the amounts below using the £ sign and decimal point,
like this: **three pounds thirty-four   £3·34**

1 five pounds sixty-three
2 eight pounds eighteen
3 sixteen pounds three
4 four pounds eighty-one
5 six pounds thirty

Write the amounts on these price labels, like this: **twenty-nine pounds ninety-five**

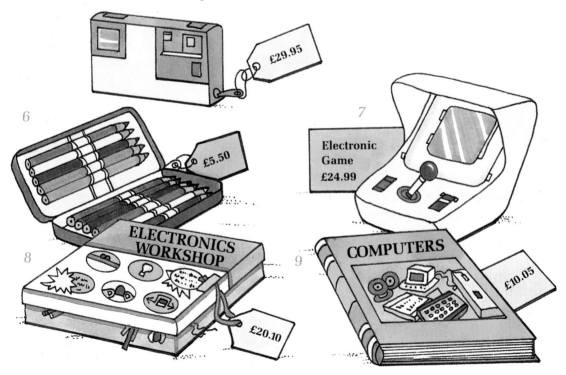

75

Change the amounts of pence below to pounds and pence, like this:

p	£
417	£4·17

1 623p

2 780p

3 607p

4 217p

5 900p

Change the amounts below to pence, like this:

£	p
£4·23	423

6 £3·90

7 £10·10

8 £6·05

9 £12·17

76

1 How many fifties are equal in value to £3?

2 How many tens are equal in value to £2?

3 How many fives are equal in value to £5?

4 How many twenties are equal in value to £4?

5 Change 20 fifties to pounds.

6 Change 30 tens to pounds.

7 Change 400 twenties to pounds.

8 Change 300 twos to pounds.

9 Change 40 fives to pounds.

77

1 How many peaches are there altogether in all the boxes?

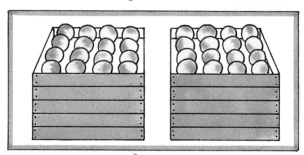

2 $100 \times 100 \times 100 = $ ▪. Write the product in words.

3 Write the correct sign ($<$, $>$ or $=$) in place of ●.

$$3 \times (40 + 40 + 40) \; ● \; 9 \times 40$$

4 Find the number which can be put in place of ▪.

$$20\,000 = ▪ + 10$$

5 4 times a number plus 6 is equal to 34. What is the number?

6 What decimal fraction of this shape is coloured?

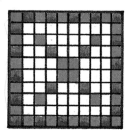

7 Find the total value of 5 fifties and 7 tens.

8 Write the correct symbol ($>$, $<$ or $=$) in place of each ●.

a $\frac{7}{100}$ ● 0·07 b 4·19 ● 4·2

9 How many fives are equal in value to 40 twos?

78

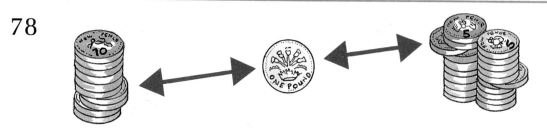

1 How many tens are equal in value to £2·90?

2 How many tens are equal in value to £10·00?

3 Change 40 tens to pounds.

4 Change 65 tens to pounds and pence.
5 How many fives are equal in value to 8 tens?
6 How many fives are equal in value to five pounds?
7 How many fives are equal in value to £2·50?
8 Change 30 fives to pounds and pence.
9 Change 22 fives to pounds and pence.

79

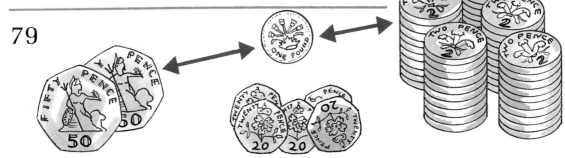

1 How many twos are equal in value to £0·70?
2 How many twenties are equal in value to £2·20?
3 Change 80 twos to pounds and pence.
4 Change 55 twenties to pounds.
5 How many twos are equal to 3 fifties?
6 How many fifties are equal in value to £9·50?
7 How many fifties are equal in value to 10 twenties?
8 Change 20 fifties to pounds.
9 How many fifties are equal in value to fifty pounds?

80

How many pence are
equal in value to:

1 4 tens and 2 fives?
2 7 tens and 7 twos?
3 2 twenties, 8 fives and
   6 twos?
4 4 twenties and 20
   pennies?
5 6 fives and 20 twos?

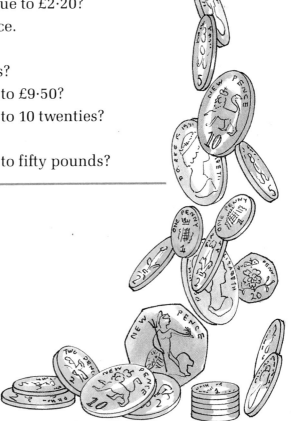

Write the total value of each
of these using the pound sign (£).

6 1 fifty and 7 tens
7 9 tens and 9 fives
8 3 twenties and 6 tens
9 2 fifties, 2 twenties and 2 fives

81

Write out each of these in full, like this:

78p = 1 fifty and 14 twos.

1 39p = 7 fives and twos
2 48p = 3 tens, 3 fives and ■ pennies
3 88p = 1 twenty, 3 tens and ■ pennies
4 £0·75 = 1 fifty and ■ fives
5 £2·60 = 8 twenties and ■ tens
6 £1·06 = 9 tens and ■ twos
7 £3·10 = 5 fifties and ■ twenties
8 £4·40 = 7 fifties, 5 tens and ■ twos.
9 £2·00 = 1 fifty, 5 twenties and ■ fives

82

1 How many people are there in this fun run?
Write the number in Roman numerals.

2 The sum of 150 and 250 is equal to the product of 40 and ■.
What is the missing number?

3 Write out this
addition in full.

```
    9 9 9
+ ■ ■ ■ ■
─────────
  2 0 0 0
```

4 There are seventeen bicycles in each of the five racks at a school.
   How many bicycles are there altogether?

5 How many centuries are there in 3000 years?

6 Arrange these fractions in order of size from the least to the greatest.

$$\frac{2}{3} \qquad \frac{5}{6} \qquad \frac{1}{2} \qquad \frac{2}{6}$$

7 Tom gave $\frac{3}{5}$ of his 20 conkers for 4 of David's. How many
   conkers did Tom have then?

8 $7 \cdot 07 = 7 + \frac{7}{\blacksquare}$

9 A bank supplied £15 worth of fives. How many coins were there?

83

3p each

8p each

69p

1 What is the total cost of a pencil and 2 balloons?

2 What is the total cost of a balloon and 2 pencils?

3 What is the total cost of a balloon, a pencil and a ball?

4 $17p + 13p = \blacksquare p$

5 $66p + 23p = \blacksquare p$

6 $15p + 55p = \blacksquare p$

7 $6p + 17p + 14p = \blacksquare p$

8 $23p + 18p + 7p = \blacksquare p$

9 $35p + 42p + 18p = \blacksquare p$

84

1 95p + 25p = £ ▮
2 £0·86 + £0·20 = £ ▮
3 78p + 31p = £ ▮
4 60p + 70p + 30p = £ ▮
5 £0·80 + £0·76 = £ ▮
6 £0·20 + £0·90 + £0·40 = £ ▮
7 £0·68 + £0·41 = £ ▮
8 £0·50 + £0·05 + £0·60 = £ ▮
9 £0·72 + £0·68 = £ ▮

85

Work out the total of each of these till receipts.

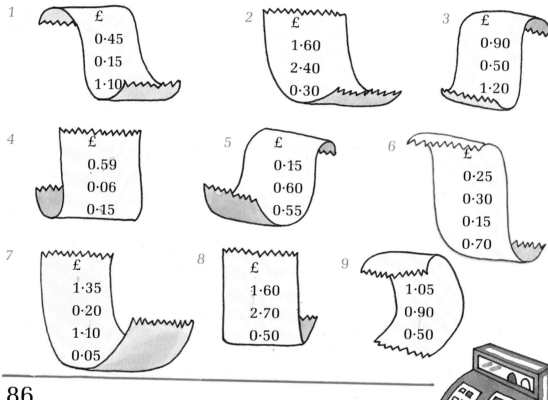

1
£
0·45
0·15
1·10

2
£
1·60
2·40
0·30

3
£
0·90
0·50
1·20

4
£
0.59
0·06
0·15

5
£
0·15
0·60
0·55

6
£
0·25
0·30
0·15
0·70

7
£
1·35
0·20
1·10
0·05

8
£
1·60
2·70
0·50

9
1·05
0·90
0·50

86

What change would you get if you spent:

1 23p out of 2 twenties?
2 13p out of a fifty?
3 £0·34 out of £1·00?
4 £1·05 out of £1·50?
5 £2·50 out of £5?
6 £1·95 out of £5?
7 £0·85 out of £10?
8 £10·10 out of £20?
9 £9·99 out of £50?

87

1 Which digit is in the hundred thousand place?

2 Find the sum of fifty thousand and 550 500 and write the answer in digits.

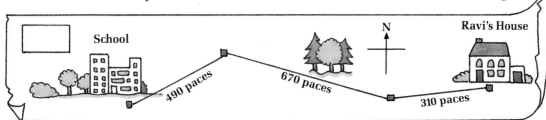

3 This sketch map shows the route from Ravi's house to school.
   a What is the total number of paces Ravi counted?
   b What direction is the school from his home?

4 $37 \times (3 \times \blacksquare) = 222$.

5 Write the correct sign ($<$, $>$ or $=$) in place of ●.
   $176 - 77$ ● 11×9

6 What fraction of these racing cars are red?

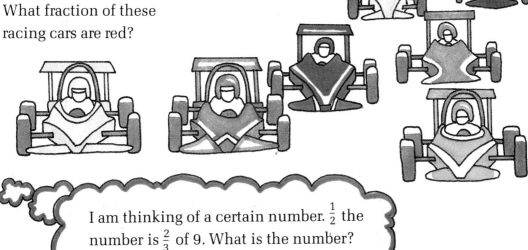

7 I am thinking of a certain number. $\frac{1}{2}$ the number is $\frac{2}{3}$ of 9. What is the number?

8 £1·50 is made up of an equal number of tens and twenties. How many coins are there altogether?

9 By how much is 2 fifties greater than 49 twos?

88

1 Take £0·80 from £2·70.
2 What is the difference between £0·90 and £0·09?
3 What is left when 75p is taken from £1·50?
4 Subtract 59p from £3·49.
5 What must be added to £0·90 to make £3·60?
6 If I had £1·10 more, I would have £11·00. How much do I have?
7 Find the difference between £1·15 and £6·30.
8 £3·30 − £0·95 = £ ■
9 If I had £1·25 left out of £3·60, how much had I spent?

89

Find the difference between these amounts.

1 £9·60 and £1·20
2 £6·10 and £5·30
3 £6·30 and £0·50
4 £11·40 and £12·35
5 £1·60 and £5·20
6 £7·00 and £2·95
7 £10·50 and £0·70
8 £16·00 and £1·60
9 £1·90 and £6·80

90

What is the cost of:

1 1 dozen balloons?
2 30 blow-outs?
3 8 eyemasks?
4 20 party hats?
5 100 face masks?
6 30 streamers?
7 10 trumpets?
8 50 headbands?
9 40 cone hats?

Party Novelties

balloons	3p	face masks	8p
blow-outs	4p	streamers	6p
eyemasks	7p	trumpets	4p
party hats	9p	cone hats	5p
headbands	10p		

91

Find the cost of:

1 3 tins of garden peas at 16p a tin
2 6 tins of baked beans at 25p a tin.
3 4 bottles of orange squash at 45p a bottle.
4 5 jars of marmalade at 55p a jar.
5 8 tins of corned beef.
6 3 packets of Crispy Crackers.
7 4 cartons of orange juice.
8 6 tins of tomatoes.
9 10 tins of peaches.

92

1 Write in digits the number which is 110 thousand more than:

2 Write in full:

$$6379 \div 10 = \blacksquare \text{ r } \blacktriangle.$$

3 From this equation: $69 \times 9 = 621$, think out the quotient to this division:

$$621 \div 69 = \blacksquare.$$

4 Find the product of 900 and 90 and 10.
5 Solve this equation: $\frac{2}{3}$ of $\blacksquare = 12$.
6 The graph below shows the distances some boys threw a cricket ball.
   What is the average distance?

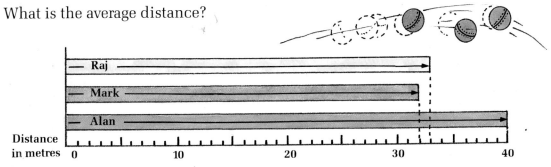

7 Write a fraction for each of these.

   a 0·3   b 0·03   c 0·33

8 3 fifties + 6 tens + $\blacksquare$ fives = £2·50
9 a £$\frac{3}{4}$ = $\blacksquare$p   b £$\frac{3}{5}$ = $\blacksquare$p

93

A school bought these books.
How much did they pay for:

1. 2 copies of *Famous Dogs*?
2. 2 copies of *Science Stories*?
3. 3 copies of *Animal World*?
4. 4 copies of *Nature Trails*?
5. 3 copies of *Picture Encyclopaedia*?
6. 6 copies of *Space Adventure*?
7. 5 copies of *World of Space*?
8. 7 copies of *Rockets*?
9. 10 copies of *Exploration*?

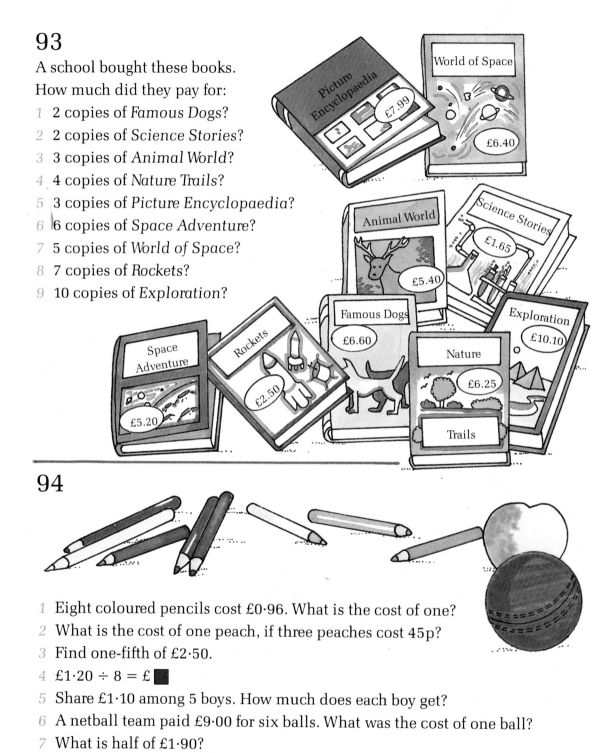

94

1. Eight coloured pencils cost £0·96. What is the cost of one?
2. What is the cost of one peach, if three peaches cost 45p?
3. Find one-fifth of £2·50.
4. £1·20 ÷ 8 = £ ▨
5. Share £1·10 among 5 boys. How much does each boy get?
6. A netball team paid £9·00 for six balls. What was the cost of one ball?
7. What is half of £1·90?
8. £5·40 ÷ 9 = £ ▨
9. £7·20 ÷ 6 = £ ▨

95

If we know the cost of 1, it is easy to find the cost of 10.

> 1 costs £0·09, 10 cost £0·90.
>
> 1 costs £0·20, 10 cost £2·00.
>
> 1 costs £0·29, 10 cost £2·90.

1 If 1 cost 4p, 10 cost £ ▪.
2 If 1 cost 11p, 10 cost £ ▪.
3 If 1 costs £0·09, 10 cost £ ▪.
4 If 1 costs 20p, 10 cost £ ▪.
5 If 1 costs 37p, 10 cost £ ▪.

If we know the cost of 1, it is easy to find the cost of 100.

> 1 costs 3p, 100 cost £3.
>
> 1 costs 30p, 100 cost £30.
>
> 1 costs 33p, 100 cost £33.

6 If 1 costs £0·07, 100 cost £ ▪.
7 If 1 costs £0·48, 100 cost £ ▪.
8 If 1 costs £4·17, 100 cost £ ▪.
9 If 1 costs £9·08, 100 cost £ ▪.

96

If we know the cost of 10, it is easy to find the cost of 1.

> 10 cost 70p, 1 costs 7p.
>
> 10 cost £0·30, 1 costs £0·03.
>
> 10 cost £2·60, 1 costs £0·26.

1 If 10 cost £0·80, 1 costs £ ▪.
2 If 10 cost £0·70, 1 costs £ ▪.
3 If 10 cost £3·00, 1 costs £ ▪.
4 If 10 cost £6·50, 1 costs £ ▪.
5 If 10 cost £43·00, 1 costs £ ▪.

If we know the cost of 100, it is easy to find the cost of 1.

> 100 cost £3, 1 costs 3p.
>
> 100 cost £45, 1 costs 45p.
>
> 100 cost £150, 1 costs £1·50.

6 If 100 cost £7·00, 1 costs £ 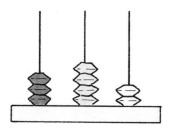.
7 If 100 cost £19·00, 1 costs £ ▪.
8 If 200 cost £16·00, 1 costs £ ▪.
9 If 100 cost £245, 1 costs £ ▪.

97

1 Multiply the abacus number by 100 and write the answer in words.

2 Find the number which is twice the product of 50 and 67.
3 Out of 1000 pupils in a school, 97 were under the age of 13.
   How many pupils were 13 and over?
4 Carl has 3 twos, 3 fives and 7 pennies. How many fruit drinks
   costing 14p each can he buy?
5 Four boxes of crayons cost £1.
   What is one crayon worth?

6 Shubi has 12 stamps, Kevin 15 and Sarah 18. If they each gave $\frac{1}{3}$ of
   their stamps to Salim, how many stamps was Salim given?

7 Arrange these numbers in order of size from the least to the greatest.

8 Write this equation in full: $\frac{\blacksquare}{100} = 0\cdot27$.

9 A train travelled 325 kilometres at an average speed of 50 kilometres per hour. How long did the journey take?

98

1 $\frac{1}{5}$ of £2·50 = $\blacksquare$p

2 $\frac{1}{10}$ of £96·00 = £$\blacksquare$

3 $\frac{3}{4}$ of £1·00 = £$\blacksquare$

4 $\frac{2}{3}$ of £1·20 = £$\blacksquare$

5 $\frac{1}{3}$ of £1·80 = £$\blacksquare$

6 $\frac{1}{8}$ of £2·40 = £$\blacksquare$

7 $\frac{1}{4}$ of £2·00 = £$\blacksquare$

8 $\frac{3}{8}$ of £3·20 = £$\blacksquare$

9 $\frac{2}{5}$ of £4·50 = £$\blacksquare$

99

A school bought prizes for a Christmas party.

1 How many combs were bought for £2·00?

2 How many whistles were bought for £1·80?

3 How many balloons were bought for £0·54?

4 How many notebooks were bought for £7·20?

5 How many diaries at 60p each were bought for £3·00?

6 How many packets of balloons at 15p a packet were bought for £3·00?

7 How many crackers at 20p each were bought for £5?

8 How many felt pens at 30p each were bought for £3·30?

9 How many party masks at 15p each were bought for £1·35?

Length

100

1 Write in digits the number which is
a hundred thousand more than a million.

2 Write the correct symbol (>, < or =) in place of ●.
938 + 629 ● 918 + 679

3 Solve this equation:
100 × **n** = one hundred and twenty thousand.

4 What fraction of the shapes are:
a triangles? b squares?

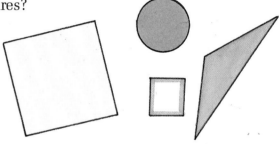

5 Write an equation for this problem.
Three times a certain number plus seven equals thirty.

6 This diagram shows how Abdul spent his money.

| Fruit drinks | Books | Skating |

If he spent 30p on fruit drinks, how much money did he have at first?

7 Ann has £1·20 in coins. Half of her money is in fives and the rest in twos.
How many coins does she have?

8 What change would be received from a £5 note after
spending £1·09 and £3·21?

9 A stack of fifteen thousand pennies was given to a charity.
What was the value in pounds?

101 | 100 centimetres = 1 metre

Paul's height is one metre nineteen, that is 1 metre and 19 centimetres.

$$1 \text{ centimetre is } \frac{1}{100} \text{ metre} = 0\cdot01 \text{ metre}$$
$$19 \text{ centimetres is } \frac{19}{100} \text{ metre} = 0\cdot19 \text{ metre}$$

Paul's height is 1·19 m.

Write these heights in metres.

1 1 metre and 45 centimetres

2 1 m 3 cm

3 128 cm

4 1 m 22 cm

5 1 metre and 40 centimetres

Write these measurements in centimetres.

6 1·07 m

7 4·20 m

8 3·19 m

9 9·07 m

102

Very small measurements are made in **millimetres (mm)**.

Here is part of a ruler marked off in centimetres and millimetres.

1 How many mm are there in 9 cm?

2 How many mm are there in $5\frac{1}{2}$ cm?

3 How many mm are there in 30 cm?

4 59 mm = ■ cm ▲ mm

5 290 mm = ■ cm

| 38 mm = 3 cm 8 mm or 3·8 cm |

6 47 mm = ■ cm   7 65 mm = ■ cm

8 2·3 cm = ■ mm   9 4·8 cm ■ mm

103

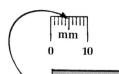

1000 millimetres = 1 metre

| **1 mm = one thousandth of a metre = 0·001 m** |

$$39 \text{ mm} = \frac{39}{1000} \text{ m} = 0·039 \text{ m}$$

$$145 \text{ mm} = \frac{145}{1000} \text{ m} = 0·145 \text{ m}$$

Write these in metres.

1 437 mm

2 28 mm

3 106 mm

4 9 mm

5 1 m 43 mm

Write these in millimetres.

6 3·786 m

7 0·038 m

8 0·004 m

9 7·109 m

104

| $\frac{1}{2}$ m = 50 cm = 0·50 m |

Write these in cm.

1 $\frac{1}{4}$ m

2 $\frac{3}{4}$ m

3 $2\frac{1}{4}$ m

4 $\frac{1}{10}$ m

5 $\frac{7}{100}$ m

| $\frac{1}{2}$ m = 500 mm = 0·500 m |

Write these in mm.

6 $\frac{4}{1000}$ m

7 $2\frac{1}{2}$ m

8 $\frac{1}{8}$ m

9 $1\frac{1}{4}$ m

105

1 Write this numeral in words.

2 $101 \times 98 = $ ■

3 The product of two factors is 96. The factors are 16 and ■.

4 Find the average of these amounts of money.

   £3·40   £1·20   £1·40

5 Write a multiplication equation to show the number of chairs in this school hall.

6 How many tennis balls costing £0·90 each can you buy with £27·00?

7 Find the number when:

   a $\frac{2}{3}$ of the number is 8,   b $\frac{3}{4}$ of the number is 24.

8 This diagram shows how the children of Parkview School come to school. What fraction of the children walk? Write the fraction in its lowest terms.

9 There are 300 pupils at Parkview School. How many come to school by coach?

106

The length of this bar is **7 cm** or **0·07 m**.

Give the length of each of these bars, first in centimetres, then in metres.

1

2

3

4

5

The length of this bar is **49 mm** or **4·9 cm**.

Give the length of each of these bars in millimetres, then in centimetres.

6

7

8

9

107

> Greater distances are measured in **kilometres (km)**.
> **1 kilometre (1 km) = 1000 metres (m)**

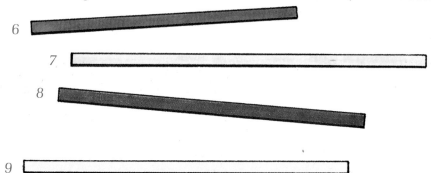

1 7 km = ▮ m
2 3 km = ▮ m
3 2 km 300 m = ▮ m
4 1 km 769 m = ▮ m
5 4 km 70 m = ▮ m
6 9000 m = ▮ km
7 8435 m = ▮ km ▲ m
8 7400 m = ▮ km ▲ m
9 2020 m = ▮ km ▲ m

108

1 metre is one thousandth of a kilometre (0·001 km).

> **9 metres** can be written **0·009 km**.
> **123 metres** can be written **0·123 km**.
> **1 km 406 m** can be written **1·406 km**.

Write these in km.

1 246 m
2 109 m
3 943 m
4 57 m
5 1327 m

Write these in m.

6 4·307 km

7 0·106 km

8 0·003 km

9 2·5 km

109

1 One-hundredth of a metre is one 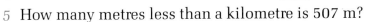.

2 One-thousandth of a metre is one ■.

3 0·1 cm = 1 ■

4 One-thousandth of a kilometre is one ■.

5 How many metres less than a kilometre is 507 m?

6 Simon lives $\frac{3}{4}$ km from school. If he stays to school dinner, how many metres does he walk each day?

7 The overall length of a car is 4535 mm. How many millimetres more than $4\frac{1}{2}$ metres is this?

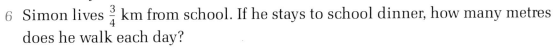

8 5 m 35 cm − 80 cm = ■ m ▲ cm

9 A length of tape measures a metre. If I use 350 mm, how many centimetres are left?

110

1 $\frac{1}{2}$ million = 500 × ■

2 Solve this equation: $7 \times (8 + \textbf{n}) = 77$.

3 In a numbers game Shuba scored 250, 75 and 50 and Krishna scored 25, 150 and 75. Who won and by how many?

4 How many notebooks can you buy with £2·10?

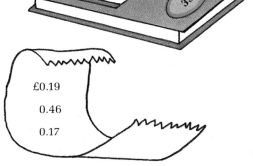

5 What change would be received from a pound after paying these amounts?

£0.19

0.46

0.17

6 The traffic count below shows the number of cars, lorries and buses which passed a school between 9.00 am and noon.

	Vehicles	Number counted
Traffic	Cars	ЖЖ ЖЖ ЖЖ ЖЖ ЖЖ ЖЖ ЖЖ ЖЖ ЖЖ
count	Lorries	ЖЖ ЖЖ ЖЖ ЖЖ ЖЖ ЖЖ I
	Buses	ЖЖ ЖЖ ЖЖ ЖЖ

How many more cars than buses were there?

7 Work out the average number of vehicles which passed the school in an hour.

8 I am thinking of a certain number. $\frac{1}{5}$ of the number is 6. What is $\frac{2}{3}$ of the number?

9 Arrange these numbers in order of size from the least to the greatest.

$$\boxed{3 \cdot 0} \qquad \boxed{0 \cdot 03} \qquad \boxed{0 \cdot 3} \qquad \boxed{3 \cdot 03} \qquad \boxed{3 \cdot 3}$$

111

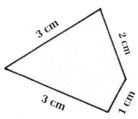

The **perimeter** of this shape is:

2 cm + 1 cm + 3 cm + 3 cm = 9 cm.

Use your ruler to find the perimeters of these shapes.

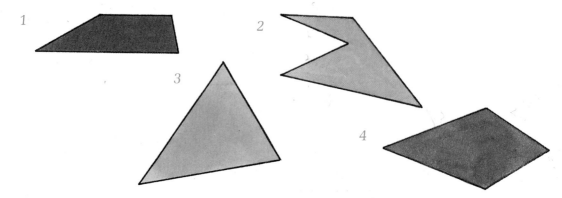

The perimeter of this field is:

20 m + 60 m + 40 m + 40 m + 30 m = 190 m.

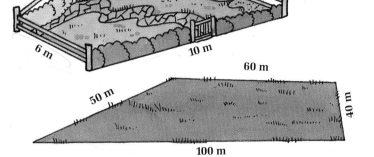

5 What is the distance around this garden?

6 What is the perimeter of this field?

7 A triangle has two sides each 90 cm. The perimeter of the triangle is 2 m. What is the length of the other side?

8 What is the perimeter of a triangular piece of cardboard with sides of 9 cm 7 mm, 4 cm 2 mm and 1 cm 3 mm?

9 The perimeter of this park is 1·5 km. What is the length of the side marked **X**?

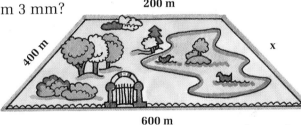

112

To find the perimeter of this hexagon we can add the lengths of the sides:

16 mm + 16 mm + 16 mm + 16 mm + 16 mm + 16 mm,

or multiply the length of a side by 6:

16 × 6 = 96 mm.

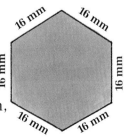

1 Find the perimeter of this square.

2 Find the perimeter of this triangle.

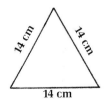

3 Find the perimeter in m and
   cm of this shape.

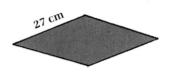

4 Find the perimeter in m and
   cm of this pentagon.

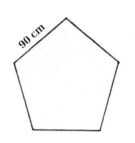

5 Find the perimeter of a
   square with sides of
   90 cm.

6 A square has a perimeter
   of 2 m. What is the
   length of a side?

7 Find the perimeter of
   this triangular garden
   if each side is
   160 m long.

8 Measure one side,
   then calculate the
   perimeter of the
   whole shape.

9 Calculate the perimeter
   in metres of this regular
   hexagon.

113

The perimeter of this
rectangle can be
found by measuring
the length and
breadth, then calculating
the perimeter like this:

$$(5 + 2) \times 2 = 14 \text{ cm.}$$

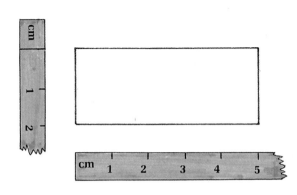

Calculate the perimeter of:

1 rectangle **a**.
3 rectangle **c**.
2 rectangle **b**.
4 rectangle **d**.

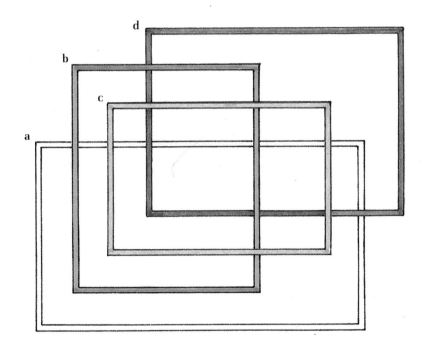

Complete each of these statements about rectangles.

5 length 16 m, width 5 m, perimeter ■ m
6 length 10 m, width 1·5 m, perimeter ■ m
7 length 96 mm, width 4 mm, perimeter ■ cm
8 length 66 cm, width 34 cm, perimeter ■ m
9 length 14 mm, width ■ mm, perimeter 50 mm

114

405 mm + 305 mm + 105 mm = 815 mm = 0·815 m

1   305 mm + 405 mm + 505 mm = ■ mm = ▲ m
2   1 m − 831 mm = ■ mm = ▲ m
3   300 mm × 5 = ■ mm = ▲ m
4   $\frac{1}{5}$ of 2 m = ■ mm = ▲ m
5   200 mm + 450 mm + 104 mm = ■ m
6   2 m − 100 mm = ■ m
7   $\frac{1}{10}$ of $2\frac{1}{2}$ m = ■ m
8   17 mm × 100 = ■ m
9   50 mm × 10 = ■ m

115

1   Add forty-five thousand to this calculator number.

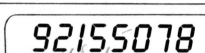

2   From 382 + 418 = 800 we know that
    382 + 418 × 1 = ■.

3   24 of the 30 pupils in David's class are 10 years of age and over. What fraction of the pupils are under 10 years of age? (Write the answer in its lowest terms.)

4   Multiply 99 by 15.

5   Write 'true' or 'false' for each of these statements:
    a (4 × 6) − 3 > 20   b (5 × 9) − 12 < 20

6   What change would you get from a pound and a fifty if you spent 70p and 45p?

7   a How many mm are there from A to B?
    b How many cm are there from A to B?

8   7 mm = ■ m

9   This pie chart shows the favourite colours of the pupils in Class 2. Twelve of the pupils prefer red. How many pupils are in the class?

Favourite colours

116

1 kilogram (kg) = 1000 grams (g)

Look at these examples:

3562 g = 3 kg 562 g = 3·562 kg

4100 g = 4 kg 100 g = 4·100 kg or 4·1 kg

Now complete these statements.

1 1639 g = ■ kg ▲ g = ◆ kg

2 4705 g = ■ kg ▲ g = ◆ kg

3 3060 g = ■ kg ▲ g = ◆ kg

4 7007 g = ■ kg ▲ g = ◆ kg

5 4800 g = ■ kg ▲ g = ◆ kg

6 7063 kg = ■ g

7 2500 kg = ■ g

8 3·1 kg = ■ g (remember 3·1 = 3·10 = 3·100)

9 4·6 kg = ■ g

117

The weight of the pears and beans can be found like this:

520 g + 590 g = 1110 g = 1·110 kg

1 Find the weight in grams of the butter and the fruit cake.

2 Find the total weight:

    a in grams,

    b in kilograms, of the butter, sardines and beans.

3 Find the total weight:

    a in grams,

    b in kilograms, of the pears, corned beef and sardines.

4 Find the total weight:

    a in grams,

    b in kilograms, of the fruit cake, and the corned beef.

What is the total in grams of each of these collections of weights?

5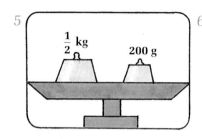

6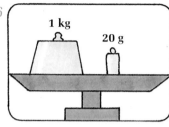

7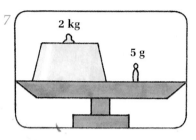

8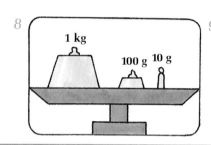

9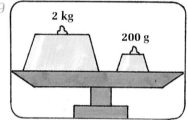

118

1. $470 \text{ g} + \blacksquare \text{ g} = \frac{1}{2} \text{ kg}$
2. $580 \text{ g} + \blacksquare \text{ g} = 1 \text{ kg}$
3. $100 \text{ g} + \blacksquare \text{ g} = 0 \cdot 250 \text{ kg}$
4. $3 \text{ kg} - 2900 \text{ g} = \blacksquare \text{ g}$
5. How many grams must be added to 7·700 kg to make 10 kg?
6. $1 \cdot 5 \text{ kg} - 700 \text{ g} = \blacksquare \text{ g}$
7. $1 \cdot 700 \text{ kg} - 900 \text{ g} = \blacksquare \text{ g}$
8. $6 \text{ g} + 60 \text{ g} + 600 \text{ g} = \blacksquare \text{ kg}$
9. $4 \text{ kg} - \frac{1}{2} \text{ kg} = \blacksquare \text{ g}$

119

Find the cost of:

1. 500 g at £1·98 per kg.
2. 250 g at £0·52 per kg.
3. 100 g at £1·20 per kg.
4. 125 g at £1·60 per kg.
5. 200 g at £1·25 per kg.
6. 2·250 kg at 24p per kg.
7. 750 g at 60p per kg.
8. 700 g at £1 per kg.
9. 1·125 kg at 80p per kg.

120

1 Write the largest number that can be shown with a four-digit numeral which has 7 as one of its digits.

2 Find the number that is four times the sum of 125 and 175.

3 How much more must be paid for four ties at £6·15 each than for four ties at £5·90 each?

£6.15   £5.90

4 £0·85 × 20 = £ ■

5 Solve this equation: $\frac{n}{9}$ of 27 = 6.

6 A coin is 1·5 mm thick. What is the height in cm of a pile of 10 coins?

7 The side of a square is 3 cm. What is the perimeter in mm of the square?

8 Out of a class of 28 pupils, 24 were present. What fraction of the class was absent?

9 a What fraction of the shape is coloured?
  b What fraction of the shape is not coloured?

121

1 What is the total weight in kg of 8 tins of beans, if one tin weighs 250 g?

2 How many tins of dog food, each weighing 0·5 kg, are there in a box holding 15 kg?

3 An empty box weighs 1·75 kg. What is the total weight in kg when the box contains 8 jars, each weighing 125 g?

4 What is the average weight of a pear?

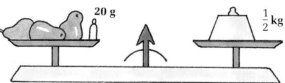

20 g $\frac{1}{2}$ kg

5 How many 50 g weights are needed to balance $\frac{1}{2}$ kg?

6 Three tins of fruit weigh 2·1 kg. What is the weight in g of one tin?

7 400 g × 3 = ■ kg

8 6 kg ÷ 4 = ■ kg

9 What is the weight in grams of the parcel on the scales?

122

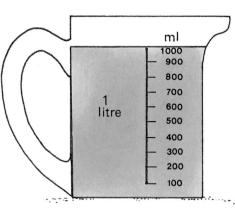

	ml
	1000
	900
	800
	700
1 litre	600
	500
	400
	300
	200
	100

> **1000 millilitres (ml) = 1 litre (1ℓ)**

1 How many ml are there in $\frac{3}{4}$ litre?
2 How many 500 ml bottles can be filled from 7 ℓ?
3 How many 5 ml doses of medicine are there in a bottle holding $\frac{1}{2}$ ℓ of medicine?
4 A medicine bottle holds 125 ml. What fraction of a litre is this?
5 How many 250 ml bottles can be filled from 3ℓ?
6 1·5 litres of milk were shared equally among 5 children. How many ml did each child get?
7 2367 ml = ■ ℓ and ▲ ml
8 4069 ml = ■ ℓ and ▲ ml
9 3ℓ and 30 ml = ■ ml

123

> 4300 ml = 4ℓ 300 ml = 4·300 ℓ
> 2060 ml = 2ℓ 60 ml = 2·060 ℓ

Now complete these.
1 3900 ml = ■ ℓ and ▲ ml = ▼ ℓ
2 4600 ml = ■ ℓ and ▲ ml = ▼ ℓ
3 5400 ml = ■ ℓ and ▲ ml = ▼ ℓ
4 2150 ml = ■ ℓ and ▲ ml = ▼ ℓ
5 6050 ml = ■ ℓ and ▲ ml = ▼ ℓ
6 3·100ℓ = ■ ℓ ▼ ml
7 2·700ℓ = ■ ℓ ▼ ml
8 1·750ℓ = ■ ℓ ▼ ml
9 5·050ℓ = ■ ℓ ▼ ml

124

> **If 1 litre of milk weighs 1·030 kg,**
> 10 litres of milk weigh 1·030 × 10 = 10·3 kg.
> 100 litres of milk weigh 1·030 × 100 = 103 kg.
> 1000 litres of milk weigh 1·030 × 1000 = 1030 kg.

1   1·150 km × 10 = ■ km
2   4·605 km × 1000 = ■ km
3   2·473 km × 100 = ■ km
4   1·5 ℓ × 10 = ■ ℓ
5   2·85 ℓ × 10 = ■ ℓ

> **If 1000 magazines weigh 35 kg,**
> 100 magazines weigh 35 ÷ 10 = 3·5 kg.
> 10 magazines weigh 35 ÷ 100 = 0·35 kg.
> 1 magazine weighs 35 ÷ 1000 = 0·035 kg.

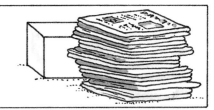

6   4637 kg ÷ 1000 = ■ kg
7   387·3 km ÷ 10 = ■ km
8   47 ℓ ÷ 100 = ■ ℓ
9   473 kg ÷ 100 = ■ kg

125

1   The Atlantic Ocean covers an area of about 12 000 000 square kilometres.
   Write this number in words.
2   The kilometre reading of a taxi was 9350 kilometres. A week later the reading
   was 10 750 kilometres. What was the daily average distance travelled?
3   A car uses 7 litres of petrol every 100 kilometres. How many litres would it use
   on a tour of 1500 km?
4   Solve this equation: (4 × 7) + 8 = (6 × n) − 12.
5   £4·50 ÷ 30 = £ ■
6   Write the next two numbers in the sequence below.
   1·35, 1·7, 2·05, ■, ■
7   What is the perimeter in millimetres of the star on the right?
8   600 m + ■ m = 1·5 km
9   Change 0·48 to a fraction in its lowest terms.

126

The time shown by this clock can be written in two ways:
11.20 or 20 past 11.

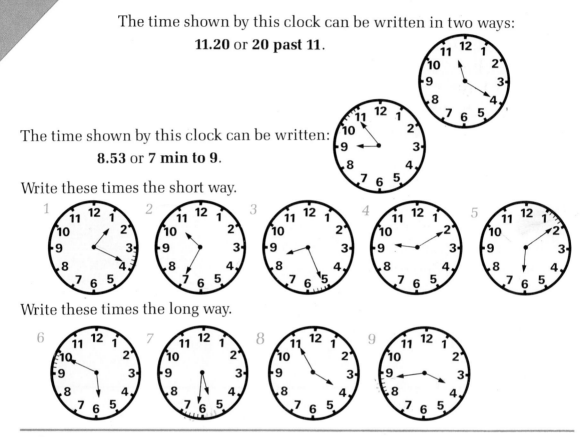

The time shown by this clock can be written:
8.53 or 7 min to 9.

Write these times the short way.

1   2   3   4   5

Write these times the long way.

6   7   8   9

127

On some timetables twenty-five minutes past two in the morning is written
2.25 am and twenty minutes to three in the afternoon is written **2.40 pm**.
Write these times, using am or pm.

1 twenty minutes past seven in the evening
2 nineteen minutes past three in the afternoon
3 twenty-five minutes to two in the morning
4 seven minutes to eleven in the morning
5 a quarter to one in the afternoon
6 Write in words 6.55 am.
7 Write in words 12.55 pm.
8 Write in words 12.10 am.
9 Write in words 7.33 pm.

128

1 How many seconds are there in $1\frac{1}{4}$ minutes?

2 How many seconds are there in $\frac{2}{3}$ minute?

3 Change 220 seconds (s) to minutes (min) and seconds.

4 $10\frac{3}{4}$ min = ■ s

5 7 min 50 s = ■ s

6 How many minutes are there in $1\frac{3}{4}$ hours (h)?

7 How many minutes are there in $3\frac{1}{4}$ hours?

8 109 min = ■ h ▲ min

9 210 min = ■ h

129

Between 2.40
and 3.05
there are 25 minutes.

How many minutes are there between:

1 7.10 and 8.00?

2 6.23 and 7.00?

3 10.15 and 11.05?

4 11.03 and 12.00?

5 2.26 and 3.05?

6 8.56 and 9.20?

7 4.42 and 5.35?

8 7.55 and 8.48?

9 2.17 and 3.15?

130

1 How many times greater is the red 5 than the blue 5?

52151

2 ■ × 100 = 30

3 Find the average of the amounts below.

£0·90   £3·00   £0·60

4 $(\frac{1}{2}$ of 96$) - (\frac{1}{3}$ of 96$)$ = ■

5 Write the length of the bar above   a in mm,   b in cm,   c in m.

6 $\frac{1}{10}$ of $\frac{1}{2}$ m = ■ mm

7 Work out the cost of buying 2 books at £4·95 each.

8 I am thinking of a number. If I add 8 to the number, it will equal $\frac{3}{4}$ of 60. What is the number?

9 Peter is 0·85 m tall. His sister Ann is 35 cm taller than he is. Their mother is 33 cm taller than Ann. What is their mother's height in m?

131

Most timetables use the 24-hour system.

9.00 am is written **09 00**   **9.00 pm** is written **21 00**

7.35 am is written **07 35**   **7.35 pm** is written **19 35**

Here is part of the Paddington to Oxford train timetable.

Paddington	dep	06 50	07 25	08 05	08 50	09 05	10 25
Oxford	arr	08 00	08 38	09 10	09 50	10 50	11 16
Paddington	dep	11 10	12 10	12 50	13 05	13 10	14 25
Oxford	arr	11 55	12 58	13 58	14 05	14 12	15 14
Paddington	dep	15 05	16 10	17 05	17 27	17 42	18 07
Oxford	arr	16 13	17 16	18 03	18 33	18 43	19 00
Paddington	dep	20 05	20 35	21 05	22 05	23 05	23 40
Oxford	arr	21 03	21 32	22 04	23 08	00 13	00 40

How many minutes are taken by the train which leaves Paddington at:

1 10 minutes to 7 in the morning?

2 25 minutes past 10 in the morning?

3 10 minutes past 1 in the afternoon?

4 25 minutes past 2 in the afternoon?

5 18 minutes to 6 in the afternoon?

6 7 minutes past 6 at night?

7 8.35 pm?

8 5 minutes past 11 at night?

9 20 minutes to midnight?

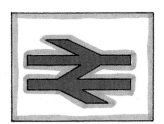

132

EDINBURGH – KING'S CROSS

Edinburgh	dep	07 35	08 35	09 35	10 40	10 55	11 35	12 35
King's Cross	arr	12 19	13 23	14 19	15 10	16 00	16 22	17 20
Edinburgh	dep	13 35	14 35	15 35	16 35	22 35	23 20	23 45
King's Cross	arr	18 26	19 24	20 22	21 31	06 49	06 05	07 00

Use the timetable to work out in hours and minutes the time taken by the train that leaves Edinburgh at:

1 07 35
2 10 40
3 10 55
4 13 35
5 15 35
6 16 35
7 22 35
8 23 20
9 23 45

133

Change these times to 12-hour clock times, using am and pm.

1
2
3

Write the times below, using the 24-hour system.

4

morning

5

afternoon

6

evening

Give the 24-hour clock time for:

7 one minute before midnight.

8 one minute after midnight.

9 10.22 pm.

134

Use the calendar to help you with these questions.

Do not count the first day unless the dates are **inclusive**.

How many days are there from:

1 1st August to 4th September?

2 17th August to 1st October?

3 8th September to 9th October?

4 20th September to 9th November?

5 30th September to 1st December?

6 1st September to 1st January?

7 20th October to 20th December?

8 10th November to 31st December?

9 Halloween to Christmas Day, inclusive?

JULY	AUGUST
S M T W T F S	S M T W T F S
1 2 3 4	1
5 6 7 8 9 10 11	2 3 4 5 6 7 8
12 13 14 15 16 17 18	9 10 11 12 13 14 15
19 20 21 22 23 24 25	16 17 18 19 20 21 22
26 27 28 29 30 31	23 24 25 26 27 28 29
	30 31

SEPTEMBER	OCTOBER
S M T W T F S	S M T W T F S
1 2 3 4 5	1 2 3
6 7 8 9 10 11 12	4 5 6 7 8 9 10
13 14 15 16 17 18 19	11 12 13 14 15 16 17
20 21 22 23 24 25 26	18 19 20 21 22 23 24
27 28 29 30	25 26 27 28 29 30 31

NOVEMBER	DECEMBER
S M T W T F S	S M T W T F S
1 2 3 4 5 6 7	1 2 3 4 5
8 9 10 11 12 13 14	6 7 8 9 10 11 12
15 16 17 18 19 20 21	13 14 15 16 17 18 19
22 23 24 25 26 27 28	20 21 22 23 24 25 26
29 30	27 28 29 30 31

135

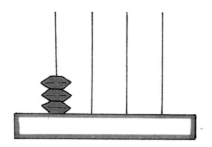

1 We know that the Roman numeral for a thousand is M.
   Write the abacus number above in Roman numerals.

2 Find the difference between the sum of 7 and 8 and the product of 7 and 8.

3 If you gave a £10 note for 2 articles, each costing £2·98, what change would you receive?

4 The perimeter of a square is 80 mm. What is the length in cm of a side?

5 What is this weight shown in the picture

  a in grams?   b in kilograms?

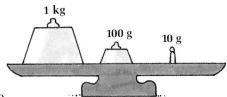

6 What is 7480 metres to the nearest kilometre?

7 A racing car completed 100 circuits in an average time of 90 seconds a circuit. How many minutes did the car take?

8 The 28th July was a Friday. What was the date of the following Wednesday?

9 Rani bought this clock/radio and paid for it at the rate of 50p per week. How many weeks did she take?

£23.50

136

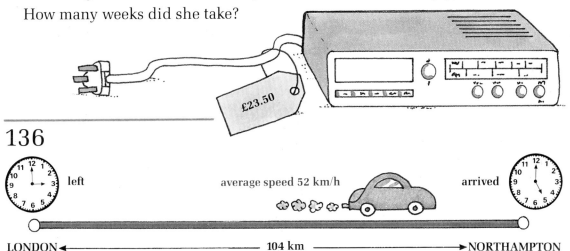

left   average speed 52 km/h   arrived

LONDON ◄——————— 104 km ———————► NORTHAMPTON

1 A cyclist travelled 51 km in 3 hours. What was his average speed in kilometres per hour (km/h)?

2 An aircraft flew 6400 km in 4 hours. What was its average speed in km/h?

3 Work out the average speed of a train which completed a journey of 420 km in 3 hours.

Work out these speeds in km/h.

4 78 km in 30 minutes   5 90 km in $1\frac{1}{2}$ hours

6 100 km in 10 minutes   7 78 km in 3 hours

8 11 km in 10 minutes   9 5 km in 12 minutes

137

> Speed of aircraft 1500 km/h
> Distance in 4 h $1500 \times 4 = 6000$ km

1 A train travelled at an average speed of 70 km/h. How far did it travel in 1 hour and 30 minutes?

2 If a cyclist travelled at an average speed of 24 km/h, how far would she cycle in 45 minutes?

3 A plane flew for $2\frac{1}{2}$ hours at an average speed of 1200 km/h. What distance did it fly?

Work out the distances travelled at:

4 56 km/h for 15 minutes.

5 60 km/h for 17 minutes.

6 30 km/h for 50 minutes.

7 48 km/h for 20 minutes.

8 80 km/h for 90 minutes.

9 100 km/h for $3\frac{1}{2}$ hours.

138

distance	90 km
speed	60 km/h
time	$\frac{90}{60} = 1\frac{1}{2}$ hours

1 An aircraft covered a distance of 800 km at an average speed of 600 km/h. How long did it take?

2 The distance from London to Huddersfield is 304 km. A motor cyclist did the journey at an average speed of 38 km/h. How long did he take?

Work out the time taken on each of these journeys.

3 100 km at 40 km/h   4 60 km at 90 km/h

5 180 km at 45 km/h   6 75 km at 30 km/h

7 79 km at 60 km/h   8 60 km at 80 km/h

9 17 km at 30 km/h

139

1 Express 720 km/h in km/min (km per min).
2 Express 90 km/h in km/min.
3 Express 45 km/h in km/min.
4 Travelling at 20 km/h, how long will it take to go 1 km?
5 Travelling at 12 km/h, how long will it take to go 1 km?
6 Travelling at 5 km/h, how long will it take to go 1 km?
7 What speed in km/h is 2 km in 3 min?
8 What speed in km/h is 5 km in 12 min?
9 What speed in km/h is 7 km in 15 min?

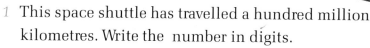

140

1 This space shuttle has travelled a hundred million
   kilometres. Write the number in digits.
2 $27 \times 5 \times 4 \times 5 =$
3 Find the sum of the numbers between 10 and 20 which are divisible by
   both 2 and 3.
4 How many seconds are there in one-third of an hour?
5 The sum of two numbers is 40 and their difference is 10.
   What are the numbers?
6 A shopkeeper bought 6 ballpoint pens for £0·85. He sold them to make a total
   profit of 35p. How much did he charge for each pen?
7 Calculate the speed in kilometres per hour of 3 km in $7\frac{1}{2}$ minutes.
8 A playground is twice as long as it is wide. If it is 20 metres wide, what is the
   distance round it?
9 This thermometer shows the temperature at 6 am.
   The temperature rose 10°, then fell 6°. What was
   the temperature then?

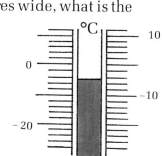

We have already learned that the best unit shape to use for surface measurement (**area**) is the square. The **area** of this shape is **14 square units** when 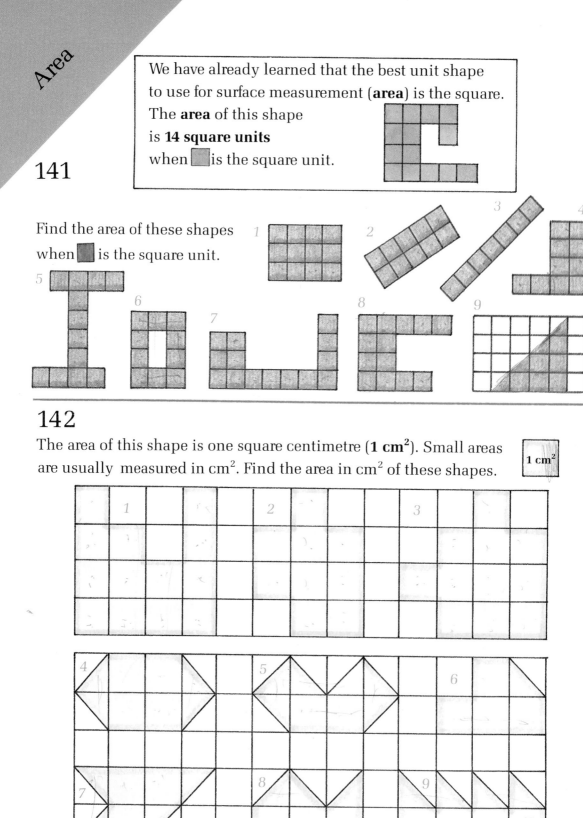 is the square unit.

Find the area of these shapes when ▮ is the square unit.

1   2   3   4

5   6   7   8   9

142

The area of this shape is one square centimetre (**1 cm²**). Small areas are usually measured in cm². Find the area in cm² of these shapes.

1 cm²

1   2   3

4   5   6

7   8   9

143

We can calculate the area of rectangles without counting each square.

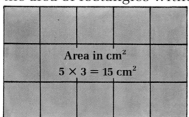

Area in cm²
5 × 3 = 15 cm²

There are 5 squares in a row and there are 3 rows.

Measure the number of cm in the length and breadth of each of these rectangles and calculate the area.

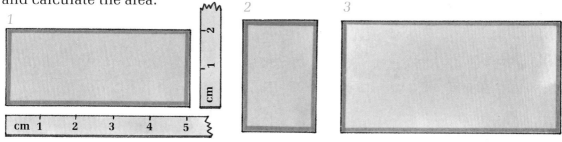

Calculate the area of these rectangles.

4 30 cm by 7 cm

5 11 cm by 10 cm

6 20 cm by 11 cm

7 14 cm by 9 cm

8 12 cm by 10 cm

9 a square with 7 cm sides

144

Larger areas are calculated in **square metres (m²)**, like this:

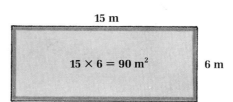

15 m

15 × 6 = 90 m²

6 m

1 What is the area of a rectangle 20 m by 50 m?

2 Calculate the area of a square with sides of 10 m.

3 Work out the area of a garden 45 m long and 20 m wide.

4 Find the area of a square with sides of 30 m.

5 A square lawn has a perimeter of 80 m. What is its area?

6 A square has an area of 81 cm². What is the length of a side?

7 A rectangle has an area of 96 cm². If the length of the rectangle is 12 cm, what is the breadth?

8 A rectangle has an area of 100 cm². Its breadth is 4 cm. What is its length?

9 A square has an area of 64 m². What is its perimeter?

145

1 Write in digits the number which is ten thousand less than a million.

2 The sum of two numbers is 500.
One of the numbers is 350.
What is the difference between the two numbers?

3 What fraction of the shape on the right is orange?

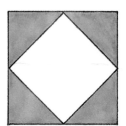

4 John has 50 marbles. David has $\frac{3}{5}$ of that number.
How many marbles do they have altogether?

5 a $4\frac{1}{3} = \frac{\blacksquare}{3}$ b Write $\frac{14}{5}$ as a mixed number.

6 How many coins were handed to the shopkeeper, if this cycle lamp was paid for with 10 fifties and the rest in tens?

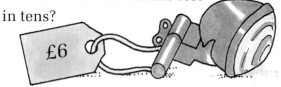

£6

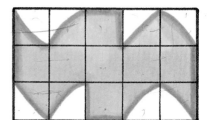

7 Estimate the area of this shape in cm^2.

8 A square has sides of 7 cm. Calculate:
a its perimeter, b its area.

9 A racing car completed 50 laps in 5 hours. What was the average lap time in minutes?

146

1 If you divide me by 7, you get a quotient of 8 and a remainder of 4. Who am I?

2 There are 50 envelopes in a packet. I need 5000 envelopes. How many packets do I need?

3 Take 12 times 659 from 22 × 659.

4 How many sheets of paper are there in the full box?

5 How many twenty-fives are there in $2\frac{1}{2}$ thousand?

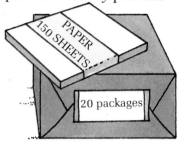

150 PAPER SHEETS

20 packages

6 The product of three numbers is 120. If the greatest is 15 and the smallest 2, what is the other number?

7 What is the total cost of all the cans of juice?

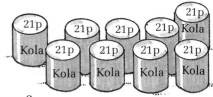

8 How many seconds are there in quarter of an hour?

9 Usha had a packet of a hundred stamps. She placed eight stamps in each row.

    a How many full rows were there?

    b How many stamps were left over to start another row?

147

1 What is the average price of the torches?

2 Share £6·30 equally among 5 girls and 4 boys. How much will each get?

3 If a dozen cost 13p, how many can you buy for £1·30?

4 If 10 cost 21p, how much does a hundred cost?

5 Jenny paid for a book with 12 twenties and 5 fifties. What was the price of the book?

6 What change would there be after buying the card and the car?

7 Rajiv has £3·30, Elizabeth has £1·10 and Sam has £0·60. How much more do they need to buy tennis balls costing £6?

8 Grapefruit are 20p each. How many could be bought for £20·20?

9 Seven girls and three boys clubbed together and each gave £2·75 for the hire of a mini-bus. What was the cost of the hire?

148

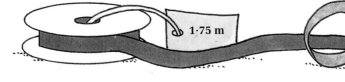

1·75 m

2 m 25 cm

1 What is the total length of tape on these two reels?
2 What is the difference between these two lengths of tape?
3 How many metres less than a kilometre is $\frac{3}{4}$ km + 50 m?
4 A length of 200 centimetres is cut from a 10 metre length of string. How many metres are left?
5 Work out the cost of 1·25 m of wire at 60p per metre?
6 How many 15 cm lengths can be cut from a length of $1\frac{1}{2}$ m?
7 Calculate the perimeter in cm of the star on the right.
8 The perimeter of a square field is $\frac{1}{2}$ km. What is the length of a side?
9 Calculate the average in cm of these lengths:

     1·30 m, 90 cm and 50 mm.

149

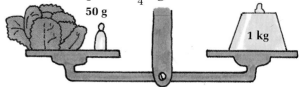

Peaches

350 g

1 The large tin is double the weight of the small tin. What is the total weight of the tins?
2 Hazelnuts weighing 725 g are mixed with 0·375 kg of almonds. What is the total weight in kg and g?
3 If a doughnut weighs 60g, what is the total weight in kg and g of 20 doughnuts?
4 Bananas weighing 500 g cost 35p. What is the cost of 5 kg of bananas?
5 How many 150 g packets of nuts can be made up from $\frac{3}{4}$ kg of nuts?
6 What is the weight of the cabbage on the scales in the picture?

50 g   1 kg

7 A cake weighing 2 kg was cut into eighths. What was the weight of each part?
8 The total weight of the apples on the right is 1·080 kg. What is the average weight of an apple?

9 If the weight of a grapefruit was 350 g, what was the total weight in kg of ten of these grapefruits?

150

1 Each of these bottles holds 350 ml of orange juice. How many litres is this altogether?

2 How many 250 ml drinking glasses can be filled from $\frac{1}{2}$ litre?

3 A $1\frac{1}{2}$ litre carton of pineapple juice was half full. How many millilitres of pineapple juice were in the carton?

4 How many 5 ml doses of medicine are there in $\frac{1}{4}$ litre of medicine?

5 How many 250 ml tins of paint can be filled from a large tin holding 2·5ℓ of paint?

6 Ten 900 ml bottles were filled from a cask holding 20 litres. How many litres were left in the cask?

7 How many 550 ml bottles can be filled from $5\frac{1}{2}$ litres?

8 The jug on the right holds 2 litres when full. About how many millilitres of juice are in the jug now?

9 What is the cost of 1750 ml at 20p per litre?

151

How many minutes are there between:

1 quarter to nine and ten o'clock?

2 twenty to seven and twenty-five to eight?

3 one forty and twenty past two?

4 2.55 am and 4.20 am?

5 7.55 pm and half past nine in the evening?

How many hours and minutes are there between:

6 10.10 am and 11.35 am?

7 11.49 pm and 2.51 am?

8 9.09 am and noon?

9 quarter past nine in the evening and midnight?

152

How many hours and minutes are there between the times shown on these clocks?

1 **00:50** and **04:30**

2 **06:05** and **10:50**

3 **11:20** and **16:00**

4 **17:00** and **03:15**

5 morning and evening

6 evening and morning

7 **AM 9:17** and **PM 3:50**

8 **PM 10:35** and **AM 12:20**

9 **AM 7:05** and **PM 5:06**

153

How many days are there from:

1 22nd October to 6th November?
2 27th February to 4th March (not Leap Year)?
3 29th January to 16th February?
4 23rd June to 7th July (inclusive)?
5 29th March to 1st May?
6 22nd August to 1st October?
7 16th September to 11th October?
8 25th April to 11th May?
9 4th November to 24th December?

154

1 If Christmas Eve is on a Friday, on what day is New Year's Eve?
2 1st April was a Sunday. What was the date of the previous Sunday?
3 How many months have 31 days?
4 1st March is a Friday. What is the date of the last Thursday in the month?
5 If the last day of June was a Sunday, what is the date of the first Saturday in June?
6 1st July is a Monday. What day of the week is the last day of July?
7 If 28th November is a Thursday, what is the date of the following Thursday?
8 If 27th May is a Monday, what is the date of the following Saturday?
9 If the last day of May is a Wednesday, what is the date of the second Thursday in June?

155

1 How many tickets were sold altogether?
2 What was the average number of tickets sold?
3 How many more books were read by the girls than by the boys?
4 What was the average number of books read?

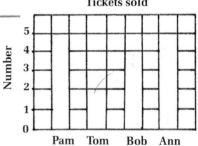

Tickets sold

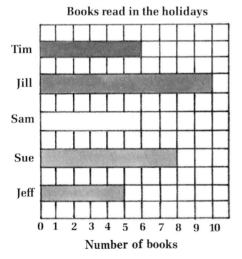

Books read in the holidays

5 What is the difference between the highest and lowest temperatures?
6 What was the average daily temperature?

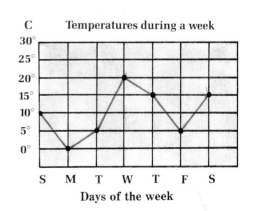

Temperatures during a week

This pie chart shows the favourite colours of
the 24 pupils in a class.

7 How many prefer yellow?

8 How many prefer blue?

9 How many prefer red?

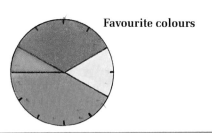

Favourite colours

156

1 The temperature shown on this thermometer is 10°C.
If the temperature fell 8°, then 4°, what would the
temperature be?

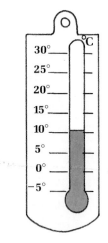

2 The temperature shown on this thermometer rose 7°,
then fell 12°. What was the temperature then?

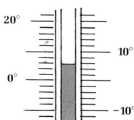

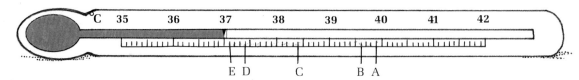

The letters show Ravi's temperature during his illness. What was the temperature
reading at:

3 A?   4 B?   5 C?   6 D?

By how many degrees did the temperature fall from:

7 A to B?   8 B to C?   9 C to E?